Houghton
Mifflin
Harcourt

S0-CFO-114

NEXT GENERATION

rBook®
Stage B

Printed in the U.S.A.

ISBN 978-0-545-31831-0

8 9 10 11 12 13 14 15 16 17   14   24 23 22 21 20 19 18 17 16 15

483368

Table of Contents

Welcome to the *rBook* 6

WORKSHOPS

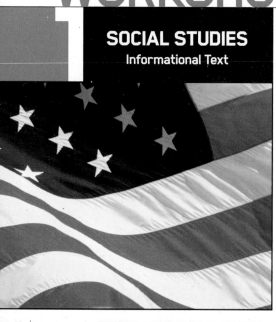

1 SOCIAL STUDIES
Informational Text

2 SCIENCE
Informational Text

Identity Crisis

LITERATURE
Literary Text
3

Stolen Childhoods 90

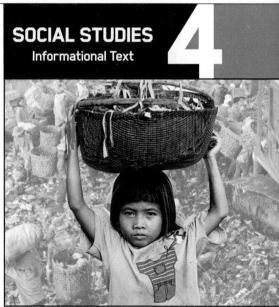

SOCIAL STUDIES
Informational Text
4

Under Pressure 118

LIFE ISSUES
Informational Text
5

6 LITERATURE
Literary Text

7 SCIENCE
Informational Text

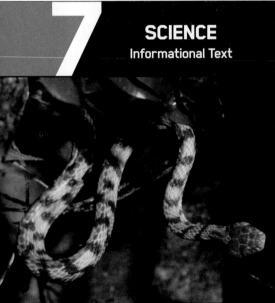

8 LIFE ISSUES
Informational Text

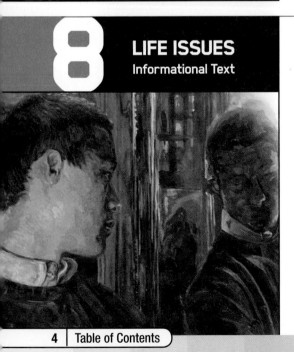

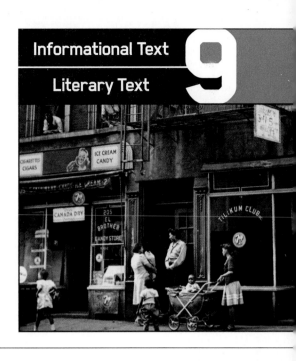

Informational Text

Literary Text

9

The Streets of Harlem

Your Resources

Content Area Icon Key

Earth Science

Earth Science

Government & Economics

Government & Economics

Health/Life Issues

Literature

Life Science

Science & Technology

The Arts

U.S. History

World Geography

Welcome to the *rBook*

Get ready for the *rBook* by taking this quiz. After you finish each Workshop, check back to see if your ideas or opinions have changed.

start

1 The New Americans

Read each statement.
Write **A** if you agree.
Write **D** if you disagree.

____ Anyone in the world should be allowed to live in the United States.

____ All newcomers to America should learn to speak English.

____ Sports stars from other countries, like Freddy Adu, should be put at the top of the list to become new U.S. citizens.

2 When Disaster Strikes

A hurricane is heading your way. What should you do? Check the action you think is wisest.

☐ You should stay in your home and keep your family, property, and pets safe.

☐ You should leave your house and go with your family to a shelter.

3 Identity Crisis

Imagine that you can change your identity. Which choice would you make? Circle it.

1. I would stay exactly who I am.

2. I would get a new life with new parents and new friends.

3. I would change some things about myself and keep other things the same.

4 Stolen Childhoods

Think about the Workshop title, "Stolen Childhoods." Look at the photos to the left and right. What do you predict this Workshop is about?

_____

_____

_____

_____

Under Pressure

5

Are teens under too much pressure? Check three pressures that you think are worst for teens today.

____ pressure to be a good kid

____ pressure to smoke

____ pressure to work hard at school

____ pressure to look good

____ pressure to fit in with friends

____ pressure to earn money

Alien Invaders

7

Check out the snakehead fish at right. This fish is an alien invader. What kinds of problems might it cause?

_____

_____

_____

Turning Points

8

Think about these tough situations.

☐ moving to a new country

☐ struggling with a serious illness

☐ finding out that a parent has gone to jail

Which situation do you think would be toughest for a teen to face? Check one.

Poe: The Master of Horror

6

Edgar Allan Poe wrote many creepy stories, including "The Fall of the House of Usher." Look at the picture of the house. Who do you imagine might live there?

☐ a creepy family with coffins in the basement

☐ a weird horror-story writer

☐ a rich vampire from Europe

☐ a clan of creatures from another world

The Streets of Harlem

9

Author Walter Dean Myers grew up in Harlem. Sometimes he got into trouble—then he had to decide what to do about it. How do *you* handle trouble? Read each statement. Write **A** if you agree. Write **D** if you disagree.

____ If I do something wrong, I don't admit it until I have to.

____ I think honesty is always the best policy.

____ If I get into trouble, I ask my family for help.

finish

WORKSHOP 1

INFORMATIONAL TEXT

COMPREHENSION FOCUS
Main Idea and Details

CRITICAL READING FOCUS
Analyze

The NEW Americans

Where do Americans come from? They come from all over the world. They come from China, Mexico, Europe, India, and Africa. America has always been a home for newcomers.

Why do so many people come here? Some want an education. Some want jobs. Everyone wants freedom and a better life.

Get ready to meet some new Americans. Find out how their lives have changed here. Find out how they are changing America.

Academic Vocabulary

Target Word	Meaning	Examples
► Read the Target Words. Rate each one using the scale below.*	► Read the Target Word meanings. Write in the missing words.	► Finish the Target Word examples below.
influence (p. 10) in•flu•ence (verb) ① ② ③ ④	*to change or* _____ *something*	My friends **influence** me to study more.
communicate (p. 13) com•mu•ni•cate (verb) ① ② ③ ④	*to share information*	• *I* **communicate** *with* _____ *by using* _____ • *My cousin can* **communicate** *in* _____
immigrant (p. 13) im•mi•grant (noun) ① ② ③ ④	*a person who moves from one* _____	• *My neighbor is an* **immigrant** *from* _____ • *A new* **immigrant** *might have to learn* _____
policy (p. 14) pol•i•cy (noun) ① ② ③ ④	*a rule*	• _____ *is a* **policy** *at my school.* • *My* **policy** *about lending money is:* _____
trend (p. 16) trend (noun) ① ② ③ ④	*a pattern of* _____ *over time*	• _____ *is a current* **trend** *at my school.* • *I do/do not (circle one) follow fashion* **trends** *because* _____

*Rating Scale
① = I don't know the word. ③ = I think I know the word.
② = I've seen it or heard it. ④ = I know it and use it.

The Key Idea

▶ **WRITE** What is this news article mostly about?

_____

_____

VOCABULARY
Target Word

currently

cur•rent•ly (adverb)

Rate It: ① ② ③ ④

Meaning

at the present

Example

I get information that is currently in the news from

_____

_____

React and Write

▶ **WRITE** Freddy turned down $750,000 to stay in school. Imagine you are Freddy. Do you take the money or stay in school? Explain.

Summarize

In one or two sentences, describe how Freddy became a soccer star. Include the topic and important details.

School Before Soccer

Young Soccer Star Shines

Freddy Adu loves to play soccer.

March 5, 2010—Freddy Adu is a talented young soccer player. At only 15, he began playing for pro teams. It was a lot for a teen to handle. Yet for Freddy, school—not soccer—always came first.

Freddy's family moved to America from Ghana when he was eight. His parents wanted a better education for their kids.

In the U.S., Freddy worked hard at school. But he missed playing soccer with his friends. One day, Freddy was practicing. A classmate saw him play. He asked Freddy to join his soccer team. Soon, Freddy became their star player.

Freddy's fame grew. Large crowds came to his games. An Italian team even made Freddy an offer. They wanted to pay him $750,000 to play!

Then Freddy's mom stepped in. She reminded Freddy why they came to America. Her words influenced him. Freddy rejected the team's offer. He focused on school instead. He studied hard enough to graduate early.

Freddy found a way to play soccer and finish school. He graduated at age 14! He also joined his hometown pro team. **Currently**, Freddy plays for a soccer team in Greece. Both of Freddy's dreams —school and soccer— have come true. ⟨END⟩

Words to Know! **rejected** turned down

Comprehension Focus
Main Idea and Details

The **main idea** is the most important point about a topic. **Details** are the facts that support the main idea. To find the main idea and details:

- Decide what the topic is. Find the main idea about the topic.
- Look for details that support the main idea.

▶ **Complete this chart with the main idea and details of "School Before Soccer."**

Detail

Freddy is very talented at soccer.

_____

_____

_____

Detail

_____

_____

_____

_____

Main Idea

_____

_____

_____

_____

Detail

_____

_____

_____

_____

Detail

_____

_____

_____

_____

💡 The Key Idea

▶ **WRITE** What is this profile mostly about?

_____

_____

◎ VOCABULARY
Target Word

income

in•come (noun)

Rate It: ① ② ③ ④

Meaning

money from _____

Example

_My_ _____ _job_

gives me a small **income**

during the _____

_____

💬 React and Write

▶ **WRITE** Moving was hard for Irene. Should she have stayed in Mexico with her grandmother? Why or why not?

FITTING IN

by Jonathan Blum

Irene Rodriguez is an immigrant from Mexico. She currently lives in Los Angeles.

It's hard to fit in when you're new in school. It's *really* hard to fit in when you're new in the country, too.

Imagine moving to a new country. You don't know your way around. You feel isolated and sad. You can't even communicate. But your parents still expect you to succeed. That's how it was for Irene Rodriguez. This young immigrant turned failure into success.

Leaving Mexico

Irene was born in a small Mexican town. When Irene was young, her dad worked 12 hours a day. But his **income** was still too small to support a family. Finally, Irene's dad moved to Los Angeles for better pay. "I didn't see him for five years," Irene says.

When Irene was nine, her family decided to join her dad. They moved to L.A., where they hoped to find a better life.

Even though life in Mexico was hard, leaving was even harder. Irene's grandmother stayed behind. "I remember leaving her," Irene says. "She cried and waved good-bye. It was so hard to look back and see her. She was getting smaller and smaller."

Strange New World

Los Angeles was a big change from Mexico. There were bright lights and tall buildings everywhere. Cars clogged the streets and noise filled the air. "I felt like I was in another world," Irene says. "I was lost."

Back home in Mexico, Irene had spent a lot of time outside. "You could ride your bike," Irene remembers. "You didn't worry that a car was going to run you over." ➤

Words to Know! **isolated** all alone

Main Idea and Details

1. ▷ **WRITE** What is the main idea in the section "Leaving Mexico"?

_____

_____

_____

2. ▷ **WRITE** What is the main idea in the section "Strange New World"?

_____

_____

_____

3. **UNDERLINE** Identify two important details that support the main idea in "Strange New World."

CRITICAL READING
Analyze

1. **CIRCLE** Identify two reasons why Irene found leaving Mexico even harder than staying.

2. ▷ **WRITE** Explain why one of those reasons made leaving Mexico harder for Irene.

_____

_____

_____

_____

_____

_____

Active Reading

UNDERLINE What advice does Irene have for new immigrants?

 VOCABULARY
Target Word

motivate

mo•ti•vate (verb)

Rate It: ① ② ③ ④

Meaning

to make someone want _____

_____

Example

Fans can **motivate** their favorite team by _____

_____

_____

 React and Write

▶ **WRITE** Who had an easier time adjusting to the U.S.—Irene or Freddy Adu? Why?

💬 Summarize

In one or two sentences, summarize the topic and important details in "Starting Over."

"Try something new," Irene says. "It will make you a better person."

Irene made friends at her new school.

Starting Over

Starting school was a struggle for Irene, too. She didn't know English. "It was frustrating," she says. "I didn't understand what people were saying."

Irene *really* hated writing in English. "Every time I wrote something, I thought people were laughing at me," she says.

Then, a bad report card made things even worse. Irene got two Fs and a D. Her dad was really angry. "I'm not sending you to school to get this type of grade," he told her. Irene got the message. Her father's words **motivated** her to learn English fast.

A Plan for Success

Irene came up with a plan. She had a friend in her English as a Second Language (ESL) class. Together, they agreed to communicate with each other only in English. "When we got stuck, we said the word in Spanish," Irene says. "But we kept everything else in English."

By high school, Irene's policy of hard work had paid off. She communicated well in English. She got better grades. She even assisted other ESL students.

Irene knows how hard it is to fit in. She has advice for new immigrants. "Try something new," Irene says. "It will make you a better person." END

| Words to Know! | assisted | helped |

Comprehension Focus
Main Idea and Details

▶ Complete this chart with the main idea and details in "Fitting In."

Detail

Detail

Main Idea

Detail

Detail

◉ The Key Idea

▶ **WRITE** What is this social studies text mostly about?

_____

_____

◉ VOCABULARY
Target Word

minimum

min•i•mum (adjective)

Rate It: ① ② ③ ④

Meaning

the _____ amount

Example

An amusement park ride might have a **minimum** height requirement because _____

_____

_____

⚠ React and Write

▶ **WRITE** The U.S. census costs billions of dollars. Is it worth the money? Why or why not?

A New Immigration BOOM

A new wave of immigrants is coming to America. Find out how they are influencing our nation.

The U.S. Census

When the U.S. census counted Americans in 2000, there were 281,421,906 of us. How does anyone count so many people? Our government sent millions of forms to homes. Most families responded by mail. Door-to-door workers tried to find everyone else. Then, everyone was counted. The census happens every ten years—and it teaches us a lot.

The census doesn't just count heads. It helps Americans *understand* America. The census asks important questions. Where were people born? What languages do they speak? When did they move here? What are their jobs?

Since 1790, census records have kept track of Americans. If you look at past records, you can see how America has changed. You can see immigration trends.

New citizens attend their swearing-in ceremony.

The New Immigrants

Where have new Americans come from? Immigration trends have changed over time. In the past, U.S. policies made it easier for people from Europe to immigrate. Up until 1965, most immigrants came from Europe. In contrast, only a **minimum** number of Asians and Latinos were allowed to immigrate. Most were rejected.

Then, in 1965, the law changed. It made immigration more fair. Soon after, a new immigration trend began. Newcomers from Asia and Latin America started settling across the country. They brought their food, music, and cultures with them.

Latino culture is having an especially big impact on our nation. Burritos are catching up with hamburgers as America's favorite food. Latino musicians sell millions of records. There are more Spanish magazines and TV shows. The census numbers help explain why. ➤

Words to Know!	**impact** effect

Main Idea and Details

1. ▶ **WRITE** What is the main idea in "The U.S. Census"?

_____

_____

_____

2. <u>UNDERLINE</u> Find two important details in "The U.S. Census."

3. ▶ **WRITE** What is the main idea in "The New Immigrants"?

_____

_____

_____

_____

_____

_____

REVIEW
Read for Detail

✔ **CHECK** Identify one detail that tells where immigrants came from after the law changed in 1965.

CRITICAL READING
Analyze

▶ **WRITE** Why does the U.S. government need to know how many people are in the country?

_____

_____

_____

Active Reading

★STAR Why are politicians paying attention to Latinos?

VOCABULARY

 Target Word

percent

per•cent (noun)

Rate It: ① ② ③ ④

Meaning

a _____

the whole

Example

I think that about _____ percent of the students in our school are _____

_____

 React and Write

▶ **WRITE** Do you think more immigration is good or bad for America? Why?

 Summarize

▶ **WRITE** Summarize the topic and important details in the social studies text "A New Immigration Boom."

A Growing Group

Look at the circle graph below about immigrants in our country. Latinos are the biggest immigrant group. They include people from Mexico, Central America, South America, and parts of the Caribbean. In 2000, they made up more than 51 **percent** of all immigrants.

Latino newcomers join other Latinos who have lived in the U.S. for centuries. In 1990, Latinos made up 9 percent of all Americans. By 2000, they had grown to 12.5 percent. They are now the largest minority group.

Politicians pay attention to this trend. They give speeches in Spanish. They join in Latino events. What motivates them? They want Latinos to vote for them!

Welcome to America?

America was founded on immigration. But are immigrants really welcome today? Yes and no. Some people say that immigration hurts America. They say that immigrants get jobs that American citizens want.

Words to Know!	**minority** a group that is less than half of the population

TEXT FEATURE Reading a Pie Chart

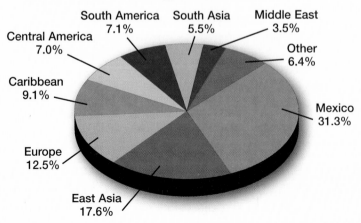

Where U.S. Immigrants Come From

Source: Center for Immigration Studies/Current Population Survey, March 2007

However, others disagree. They say immigrants help America. Many immigrants work for minimum wage. Often, American workers reject those low-income jobs.

Immigrants help in other ways, too. They move to cities that need more workers. They start businesses. They pay taxes. They become citizens. They vote.

Some immigrants are even winning political office. Arnold Schwarzenegger is the governor of California. He was a famous movie star. He's also an immigrant from Austria. "I have gotten all of the opportunities because of America," he says. "I have seen firsthand what it's like to come over here, with empty pockets but full of dreams . . . and to succeed." END

New Americans contribute to the U.S. in many ways.

A pie chart shows percentages of a whole.

❶ What information does this circle graph show?

Ⓐ how many people live in the U.S.

Ⓑ how many immigrants live in the U.S.

Ⓒ where today's immigrants come from

Ⓓ what parts of Mexico immigrants come from

❷ What color shows the percentage of immigrants from Central America?

Ⓐ blue   Ⓑ yellow   Ⓒ red   Ⓓ green

❸ **Analyze:** Most of the Latino immigrants come from

Mexico because _____

Main Idea and Details

1. ▶ **WRITE** What is the main idea of "A Growing Group"?

_____

_____

_____

2. **UNDERLINE** Mark two important details in that section.

CRITICAL READING
Analyze

▶ **WRITE** What are two benefits that immigrants bring to the United States?

1. _____

_____

2. _____

_____

Skills Check

1. ▶ **WRITE** What is the main idea of "Welcome to America?"

_____

_____

_____

2. **CIRCLE** Identify three important details in "Welcome to America?"

WORD CHALLENGE

It's my **policy** to talk to my best friend every night. That's just a **rule** for me!

START

1

Think about it. What **percent** of your day is spent:

eating? _____

sleeping? _____

watching TV? _____

being in school? _____

2

Decide. What do you think the **minimum** age should be for:

voting in an election? _____

driving? _____

serving in the army? _____

3 Synonyms

Synonyms are words that have similar meanings. Examples are *pretty* and *beautiful,* or *soldier* and *warrior.*

Match each word to its synonyms below.

communicate	irritable	policy

Synonym

rule, guideline: _____

nervous, jumpy: _____

talk, express: _____

4

Describe. What TV commercial has totally **influenced** you (meaning you *really, really* want to buy the product)?

_____

_____

_____

5

Pick one. If you were on a sports team, which statement would **motivate** you the most to win? Explain why.

☐ If you don't win, you're all getting kicked off the team!

☐ If you win, I'm treating everyone to a pizza party!

_____

_____

6

Rate it. Read each movie theater **policy**. Write **S** if the policy makes sense. Write **N** if the policy makes no sense.

____ Cell phones must be turned off.

____ No popcorn bags are allowed in the theater.

____ Movies will be turned off for a 10-minute bathroom break.

8 Antonyms

Huge

Antonyms are words that have opposite meanings. Examples are *good* and *bad,* or *miserable* and *happy.*

Match each word to its antonym below.

| isolated | currently | minority |

Antonym

formerly: _____

included: _____

majority: _____

Small

Find the Word to Know (page 10) that is an antonym of the underlined word below.

Freddy Adu <u>accepted</u> a deal with a professional team.

Write the antonym here: _____

7

Evaluate. What music do you **currently** like? List three songs.

1. _____
   _____
2. _____
   _____
3. _____
   _____

9

Finish them. Complete these sentences with **income** or **communicate**.

• The boss said, "I'm not raising your _____."

• For many teens, it's easier to _____ with their friends than with their parents.

10

Finish them. Complete these sentences with **immigrant** or **trend**.

• A new _____ might not understand American TV shows.

• A new _____ in schools is 7th graders wearing skinny jeans.

FINISH

Writing Text Type
Informational Paragraph

An **informational paragraph** provides information and explains it.

▶ **Read Melissa Chan's informational paragraph about immigration in her neighborhood.**

Student Model

Topic Sentence

The **topic sentence** states the topic of the paragraph.

1. **UNDERLINE** the topic sentence.

A strong topic sentence has a **controlling idea** that makes the writer's point about the topic.

2. **BOX** the controlling idea.

Detail Sentences

Factual details in the paragraph support the topic sentence with relevant facts, examples, and data.

3. ✔ **CHECK** three factual details.

Language Use

Transition words and phrases introduce and connect ideas in the paragraph.

4. **CIRCLE** three transition words or phrases.

The writer uses **precise verbs** to explain the information.

5. **DOUBLE UNDERLINE** three precise verbs.

Concluding Sentence

The **concluding sentence** follows logically from the detail sentences. It explains why the topic is important.

6. ★ **STAR** the concluding sentence.

The Changing Face of My Neighborhood
by Melissa Chan

Immigration has transformed the face of my Los Angeles neighborhood in positive ways. The most interesting change is the variety of people I see every day. For example, several Korean and Arab immigrants own and operate businesses along Main Street. They provide crucial services for the community. At school, 50 percent of the students in my class are immigrants, including my best friend, Maria Rios from the Philippines. Another important change is that members of my own family moved here from Guyana. In conclusion, immigrants influence the diverse cultures in my neighborhood, making it a vibrant place to live!

B *I* U

P 1

Brainstorm

▶ Read the writing prompt in the middle of the idea web.
Then use the boxes to help you brainstorm your ideas.

People

Food

Writing Prompt:
Explain how immigration has changed your neighborhood.

_____
(your neighborhood)

Language

Music

Choose Your Topic

▶ Select one of your ideas from the idea web. Then complete the sentence below.

I plan to write about _____

because it _____

_____

Organize Ideas for Writing

▶ **Complete this outline with notes for your informational paragraph.**

I. Topic Sentence. State your main point.

Topic: _____

Controlling Idea: _____

II. Detail Sentences. List two factual details that support the topic sentence.

Detail 1: _____

Detail 2: _____

III. Concluding Sentence. Restate the topic and explain why it is important.

_____

_____

Write Your Draft

▶ **Write a draft of your informational paragraph.**

Writing Prompt:
Explain how immigration has changed your neighborhood.

WORD CHOICES	
Everyday	**Precise**
different	diverse
important	crucial
changed	transformed

_____
(paragraph title)

▶ **Write your topic sentence.**

Topic Sentence

Immigration _____ my neighborhood in _____
            (topic)   (your neighborhood)

_____.
(controlling idea)

▶ **Type your topic sentence on the computer or write it on paper. Then use these transition words and phrases to complete a draft of your paragraph.**

Detail Sentences

In my neighborhood, . . .	*For example, . . .*
In addition, . . .	*In conclusion, . . .*

Concluding Sentence

In conclusion, . . .	*To sum up, . . .*

Revise Your Paragraph

▶ **Evaluate:** Rate your paragraph. Then have a writing partner rate it.

Scoring Guide			
needs improvement	average	good	excellent
1	**2**	**3**	**4**

1. **UNDERLINE** the topic sentence. Does it state the topic of the paragraph?

   Self   1   2   3   4
   Partner   1   2   3   4

2. **BOX** the controlling idea. Does it make a clear point about the topic?

   Self   1   2   3   4
   Partner   1   2   3   4

3. ✔**CHECK** the factual details. Do they include relevant facts, examples, and data?

   Self   1   2   3   4
   Partner   1   2   3   4

4. **CIRCLE** transition words and phrases. Do they introduce and connect ideas?

   Self   1   2   3   4
   Partner   1   2   3   4

5. **DOUBLE UNDERLINE** the precise verbs. Do they explain information?

   Self   1   2   3   4
   Partner   1   2   3   4

6. ★**STAR** the concluding sentence. Does it explain why the topic is important?

   Self   1   2   3   4
   Partner   1   2   3   4

▶ **Discuss:** Give feedback on your partner's informational paragraph.

1. Start with positive comments about your partner's paragraph.

   You did an effective job of _____
   _____

   You included interesting examples about
   _____

2. Give your partner suggestions for revision.

   I have a question about _____
   _____

   Your detail sentences would be stronger if you _____

   Your word choices _____
   _____

3. Answer any questions your partner has about your suggestions.

4. Ask your partner for feedback. Use the frames below to summarize your partner's feedback.

   I did an effective job of . . .
   You had a question about . . .
   You suggested that . . .
   My paragraph needs . . .

▶ **Revise** Now revise your informational paragraph.

Grammar IDENTIFYING SENTENCES AND FRAGMENTS

A **sentence** is a group of words that tells a complete idea.

- The **subject** tells who or what the sentence is about.
- The **predicate** tells what someone or something does.

Example	
Subject	**Predicate**
Irene's parents	**moved to America from Mexico.**
My neighbors	**are from China and Vietnam.**

▶ **Identify the underlined part of each sentence below. Write *subject* or *predicate* on the line beside it.**

1. My family and I watched a show about immigrants.   *predicate*

2. Three children moved here with their mother.

3. Their father came to the U.S. a year later.

4. At first, the family had very little money.

5. Finally, the father found a job working in a factory.

A **sentence fragment** is an incomplete sentence that cannot stand by itself. Often, a fragment is missing either a subject or a predicate.

Example	
Sentence Fragment	**Complete Sentence**
opened their own business [missing subject]	**The Italian brothers opened their own business.**
Many immigrant parents [missing predicate]	**Many immigrant parents want their children to grow up in the U.S.**

▶ **Rewrite the sentence fragments below as complete sentences.**

6. some immigrants from Latin America and Asia

_____

7. the plane from India

_____

8. wants to see her grandmother who lives in Mexico

_____

▶ **Edit Your Draft.** Take a close look at each sentence in your draft. **Does each sentence express a complete idea?** Fix the ones that do not.

Mechanics USING END PUNCTUATION

Different kinds of sentences use different **end punctuation marks**.

- A **statement** always ends with a period.
- A **question** always ends with a question mark.

Example

Statement	Question
I'm from Mexico.	Where are you from?
We are a nation of immigrants.	Were your parents immigrants?

▶ **Find and correct five errors in this paragraph.**

Student Model

CHECK AND CORRECT

☐ **UNDERLINE** two end punctuation errors and correct them.

☐ Correct one sentence fragment.

☐ **CIRCLE** two spelling errors and correct them.

My city, New York, has been changed a lot by imigration. See it every day. First of all, some nayborhoods are named after countries, like Chinatown and Little Italy? In addition, you can find a lot of food from other countries here. Another important thing is that I have a lot of friends from other countries. In conclusion, New York has been very influenced by immigration?

▶ **Edit Your Draft.** Look at the sentences in your own draft. **Do they all have the correct end punctuation?** Fix the ones that do not.

Final Draft/Present

▶ **Write a final draft of your paragraph on the computer or paper. Check it again and correct any errors before you present it.**

Analyze a Registration Form

Schools and programs use registration forms to collect and track information about their members.

▶ **Read this completed registration form for an after-school language club. Then answer the questions below.**

MARK IT

- **UNDERLINE** the program this registration form is for.
- **CIRCLE** the information that tells who the student is and how to contact her.
- ★**STAR** the program's schedule.

CHINESE CULTURE CLUB!

To join this after-school club, you must commit to attending twice a week. We will meet from 3:30 to 5 p.m. daily for fun activities and homework help. The registration deadline is September 15.

Lubin, Alissa	13	8
Name (last, first)	**Age**	**Grade**

Youkalis, Rachel	206-555-1234
Parent/Guardian Name	**Telephone**

Which activities would you most enjoy participating in? Check all that apply.

- ☑ Chinese cooking
- ☑ Chinese games/culture
- ☑ Chinese conversation
- ☐ Chinese calligraphy (handwriting)

What else would you like to do or learn in this club? List two goals of your own.

- *I want to be able to order food at a Chinese restaurant.*
- *I want to learn more about China and then visit China someday.*

❶ What is the deadline for registering?

- (A) September 15
- (B) There is no deadline.
- (C) before the first meeting
- (D) before school begins for the year

❷ What days would you need to commit to going to the club?

- (A) every day after school
- (B) twice a week after school
- (C) Mondays and Wednesdays before school
- (D) on weekends

❸ What after-school club would you consider joining at your school? Finish the sentences below.

A. I would consider joining a _____ _____ club.

B. One personal goal I would work on in this club is _____ _____ _____

Spanish Teacher
Pedro Gonzalez

Meet a teacher who makes learning a new language fun.

▶ **Read the interview and job information. Then answer the questions below about Pedro Gonzalez's job.**

S **Scholastic: How did you decide to become a teacher?**

Pedro Gonzalez: I didn't know what I wanted to do while I was in college. My dad and a friend encouraged me to try teaching. Unfortunately, most of my teachers were boring! I decided to be one of the fun teachers that teaches students to love learning.

S **How do you encourage your students to use their Spanish skills?**

Once, I pretended to be a server, and students placed their lunch orders with me in Spanish, and gave me money. The next day, I brought in their orders from a burrito restaurant! I also encourage students to talk to the Spanish-speaking staff at school.

S **Can anyone learn a foreign language?**

Yes, but there are different ways to learn. Some learn by listening, some by reading, some by talking. I try different kinds of activities in my class so that all students have an opportunity to learn in the way that's best for them.

---

❶ How did Pedro Gonzalez finally discover his career goal?

_____

_____

❷ How important is Gonzalez's job? Mark the line.

```
1       2       3       4       5
```
Not very important   Very important

❸ I think Gonzalez's job is/is not (circle one) **important because**

_____

_____

ON THE JOB

EDUCATION

Bachelor's degree; Master's degree in Education

RESPONSIBILITIES
- Plans classroom lessons
- Grades assignments
- Motivates students
- Develops ways for students to use what they learn in class

SKILLS
- Interacting with students
- Inspiring students to work hard
- Learning and teaching a language

SALARY

$40,000–$45,000

FAVORITE PART OF THE JOB

"Working with kids and teaching them a new language feel really important."

CAREER CONNECTION

Education and Training
www.careerclusters.org

Related Jobs
- coach
- language tutor
- translator

Should we all have to learn a new language?

For students in many schools, learning another language is a requirement. Should middle school students have to learn a new language? Have a class debate.

❶ **Consider different points of view.** Based on what you have learned in this Workshop, how could learning a new language benefit you or members of your class? How could it be challenging?

Benefits	Challenges

❷ **State your position.** Which side of the debate are you on?

We believe that middle school students _____ have to learn a new language.

❸ **Justify your position.** What details about your class or school support your position? Give specific facts and relevant examples.

Our Arguments	Our Support
a.	
b.	
c.	

④ **Prepare for the debate.** Organize your notes from the weakest point to the strongest, or vice versa. Then think ahead: How might the other side respond to your arguments?

AN EFFECTIVE DEBATE

✓ states both sides of the issue.

✓ provides examples, facts, and anecdotes to support each position.

✓ considers the other side's arguments and responds to them.

DEBATE: _Should we all have to learn a new language?_

OPENING STATEMENT: _____

_____

_____

_____

_____

OUR SIDE:

a. _____

_____

_____

_____

b. _____

_____

_____

_____

c. _____

_____

_____

_____

POSSIBLE RESPONSE:

a. _____

_____

_____

_____

b. _____

_____

_____

_____

c. _____

_____

_____

_____

SUMMARY/CLOSING STATEMENT: _To summarize, middle school students_ _be required to learn a new language because_

_____

_____

_____

Comprehension

▶ **Fill in the circle next to the correct answer.**

1. Why did Freddy Adu's family move to America?
   Ⓐ They had to escape a war.
   Ⓑ They wanted to give their kids a better education.
   Ⓒ They wanted to get better jobs.
   Ⓓ Freddy couldn't play soccer in Ghana, his home country.

Here's a Tip.
Read all the answer choices before answering a question.

CRITICAL READING

2. **Analyze:** What two factors helped Irene Rodriguez to achieve success in her Los Angeles high school?
   Ⓐ classmates who laughed at her accent / speaking Spanish
   Ⓑ starting school in the U.S. / a report card with Fs and a D
   Ⓒ moving to Los Angeles / missing her grandmother in Mexico
   Ⓓ her decision to work harder / her study plan with a friend

3. What is the main idea for this Workshop, "The New Americans"?
   Ⓐ Freddy Adu will be a huge star.
   Ⓑ Immigration has changed the United States.
   Ⓒ People are moving to Latin America.
   Ⓓ It's easy to move to the United States.

4. Most new immigrants to America are
   from _____.
   Ⓐ Latin America and Asia
   Ⓑ Asia and Africa
   Ⓒ Latin America and Europe
   Ⓓ Europe

CRITICAL READING

5. **Analyze:** Which of the following statements about immigrants is an opinion?
   Ⓐ Latinos made up 12.5 percent of the immigrants counted in the 2000 U.S. census.
   Ⓑ Immigrants are now moving to cities all over the U.S.
   Ⓒ It's easy to make it as an immigrant.
   Ⓓ Arnold Schwarzenegger is an immigrant.

Vocabulary

▶ **Fill in the circle next to the correct definition of the underlined word.**

1. It wasn't easy for Irene to be a new immigrant.
   Ⓐ someone who moves from one country to another
   Ⓑ friend
   Ⓒ student in a school
   Ⓓ pop star

2. Immigrants often influence the communities they live in.
   Ⓐ change
   Ⓑ count
   Ⓒ compare
   Ⓓ find

3. Today's music trends include an increase in the popularity of Latino music.
   Ⓐ stars
   Ⓑ languages
   Ⓒ patterns of change over time
   Ⓓ top-ten lists

▶ **Choose the synonyms for the underlined words.**

4. Our class policy is that everyone must communicate respectfully.
   Ⓐ schedule, dress
   Ⓑ room, play
   Ⓒ question, act
   Ⓓ rule, talk

▶ **Choose the antonym for the underlined word.**

5. My sister spends a minimum of five hours at the mall every weekend.
   Ⓐ extreme sport
   Ⓑ maximum
   Ⓒ least amount
   Ⓓ fast speed

Short Answer

CRITICAL READING

▶ **Analyze: Use what you've read in this Workshop to answer the question below. Check your spelling and grammar.**

What challenges do new immigrants in the U.S. face?

_____

_____

_____

_____

_____

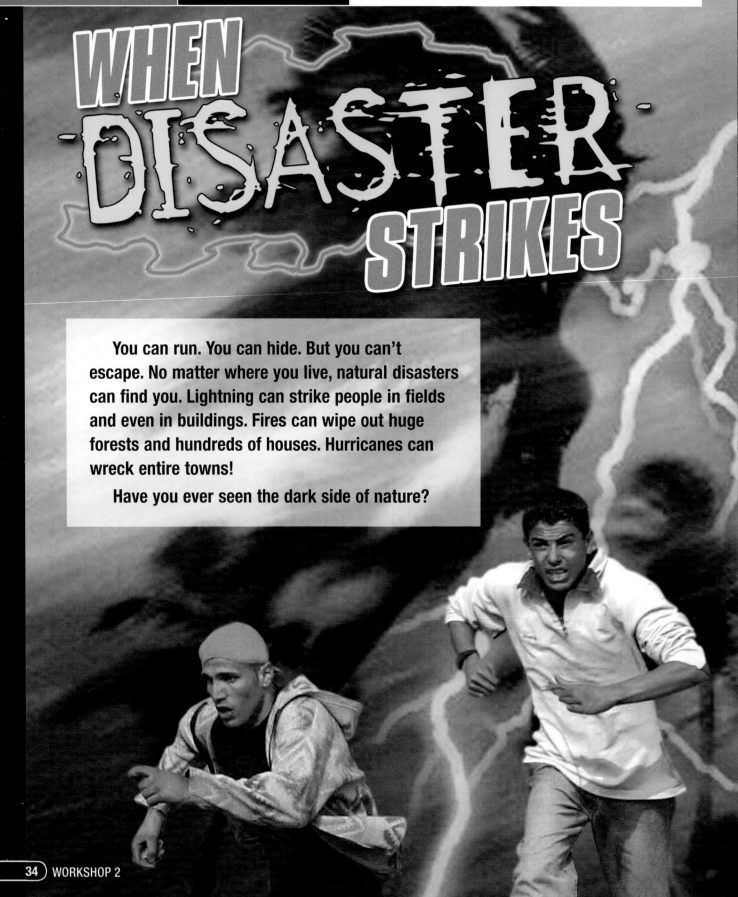

WORKSHOP 2

INFORMATIONAL TEXT

COMPREHENSION FOCUS
Sequence of Events

CRITICAL READING FOCUS
Synthesize

Reading 1 Struck by Lightning | **News Article**

Reading 2 A Mountain on Fire | **Magazine Article**

Reading 3 Hurricanes: The Monster Storms | **Science Text**

WHEN DISASTER STRIKES

You can run. You can hide. But you can't escape. No matter where you live, natural disasters can find you. Lightning can strike people in fields and even in buildings. Fires can wipe out huge forests and hundreds of houses. Hurricanes can wreck entire towns!

Have you ever seen the dark side of nature?

Academic Vocabulary

Target Word	Meaning	Examples
▶ Read the Target Words. Rate each one using the scale below.*	▶ Read the Target Word meanings. Write in the missing words.	▶ Finish the Target Word examples below.
recovery (p. 36) re•cov•er•y (noun) ① ② ③ ④	the process of getting back to normal	• For quick **recovery** from the flu, you should _____ • **Recovery** from _____ will be _____
severe (p. 36) se•vere (adjective) ① ② ③ ④	very _____ or serious	A **severe** storm is headed our way.
prevent (p. 39) pre•vent (verb) ① ② ③ ④	to _____ from happening	• The other team tried to **prevent** me from _____ _____ • One injury I would like to **prevent** is _____
destruction (p. 40) de•struc•tion (noun) ① ② ③ ④	terrible _____	• **Destruction** caused by a storm might include _____ _____ • A pet _____ caused **destruction** in _____
major (p. 42) ma•jor (adjective) ① ② ③ ④	very large or important	• A **major** event during the school year is _____ _____ • My 18th birthday will be a **major** one because _____ _____

*Rating Scale
① = I don't know the word. ③ = I think I know the word.
② = I've seen it or heard it. ④ = I know it and use it.

The Key Idea

▶ **WRITE** What is this article mostly about?

_____

_____

VOCABULARY
Target Word

focus

fo•cus (verb)

Rate It: ① ② ③ ④

Meaning

to pay close _____

_____

Example

An activity that is hard to
focus on in a noisy place is

_____

_____

React and Write

▶ **WRITE** Suppose that you saw lightning strike someone. What would you do?

Summarize

In one or two sentences, summarize what happened to Justin. Include the topic and important details.

Struck by Lightning

A teen's life changed in a flash!

September 6, 2001— Last month, 16-year-old Justin Norris headed to his after-school job at a fast-food restaurant. It seemed like an ordinary day. But it didn't stay that way for long. Justin was about to get the shock of his life!

Justin started work inside the restaurant at the counter. After an hour, he moved to the drive-through window. He took orders from customers through a big menu board. Outside, a severe storm was building. "I heard loud thunder," Justin remembers.

At first, Justin ignored the thunder and **focused** on his work. But the thunder grew louder. Soon, Justin couldn't hear his customers through the speaker. He turned up the volume knob.

Then, a powerful bolt of lightning hit the outdoor menu board. A surge of electricity rushed in. It exceeded 15 million volts! The electricity shot through the board to the knob. Finally, it slammed into

Justin Norris survived being struck by lightning.

Justin's body and knocked him out. He was rushed to the hospital.

At the hospital, Justin had seizures. He couldn't remember names and numbers. The accident had wiped out his memory.

Now Justin is on the road to recovery. Currently, he still has memory loss. But Justin is happy. Why? He knows he's lucky to be alive. ⟨END⟩

Words to Know!	**exceeded**	was greater than

Comprehension Focus

Sequence of Events

Sequence is the order in which events happen. To find the sequence of events:

• Try to remember the order in which events take place.

• Look for times, dates, and signal words, such as *first*, *then*, *next*, *after*, and *finally*.

• When you know the order, check it again. Make sure it makes sense.

▶ **Complete this chart with the sequence of events that led to Justin being struck by lightning.**

At first

Justin ignored the thunder and focused on his work.

Soon

Then

Finally

The Key Idea

▶ **WRITE** What is this article mostly about?

_____

_____

VOCABULARY
Target Word

increase

in•crease (verb)

Rate It: ① ② ③ ④

Meaning

to make or get _____

Example

*Wind can **increase** the intensity of a fire and make it* _____

_____

React and Write

▶ **WRITE** Fighting fires is a tough and dangerous job. Why would *anyone* want to become a firefighter? Would you?

A MOUNTAIN ON

by Emily Costello

This disaster destroyed a forest and killed firefighters. Find out what happened from those who survived.

The fire on Storm King Mountain in Colorado was one of the worst in U.S. history. It happened over nine hot days in July 1994.

The Flames Rise

The summer of '94 was hot and dry in Colorado. Rain didn't fall for weeks. The sun baked forests dry. Soon, dozens of fires were burning across the state. Fire crews battled the flames. But the crews were stretched thin.

Then, on July 2, flames rose up on Storm King Mountain. It was the start of what would become a monster fire.

At first, firefighters ignored it. They had bigger flames to fight. But then, the wind changed direction. The fire **increased** in size. Before long, ten acres were up in flames.

The Big Blowup

On July 3, a team of firefighters headed to Storm King. First, seven of them hiked toward the flames. They cut down trees and dug ditches. At the same time, helicopters dumped water on the flames from above.

But nothing could prevent the fire from spreading. The flames just wouldn't die. It was time to radio for help.

The second day of firefighting began. About 40 more firefighters joined the crew. At 3:20 P.M., a dry wind swept through the forest. The wind fanned the flames and blew them across a creek. Suddenly, a huge stand of oak trees burst into flames.

Then, the Storm King fire "blew up." A "blowup" is a sudden jump in a fire's intensity.

"It's going up," one firefighter shouted into his radio. "Everybody get out!" ➤

| Words to Know! | **intensity** | great strength or extreme degree |

Sequence of Events

1. **UNDERLINE** Mark five signal words or phrases that help you follow the sequence of events in "The Flames Rise."

2. ▶ **WRITE** Identify four events in "The Big Blowup."

• On July 3, _____

_____

_____

• The second day, _____

_____

_____

• At 3:20 P.M., _____

_____

_____

• Then, the Storm King fire _____

_____

CRITICAL READING
Synthesize

▶ **WRITE** How dangerous do you think a fire "blowup" is? Give evidence to support your response.

_____

_____

_____

_____

_____

_____

Active Reading

<u>UNDERLINE</u> Where did firefighters hide from the fire?

VOCABULARY
Target Word

degree

de•gree (noun)

Rate It: ① ② ③ ④

Meaning

a unit of _____

Example

Degrees of temperature tell

_____

_____

React and Write

▶ **WRITE** What would you be thinking about if you had been stuck in the fire shelter?

Summarize

In one or two sentences, summarize the topic and important details in "Run for Your Life."

The Storm King fire raged on for days.

> "I was running," one firefighter said. "I was scared to death."

Run for Your Life

The firefighters saw a wall of flames racing toward them. Everyone looked for a way out. "I was running," one firefighter said. "I was scared to death."

Tony Petrilli was the leader of a team. He told his crew to stop running. After that, he ordered his crew to open their fire shelters and crawl inside. The shelters are small metallic tents that keep out flames.

Inside their tents, the firefighters waited. Smoke choked their lungs. Heat burned their skin. Temperatures crept up to over 100 **degrees**. The firefighters knew they might die.

Burnt Out

The fire raged on for two more hours. Then, the wind died down. The flames burned more slowly. At last, the firefighters crawled out. They saw destruction everywhere. All that was left of the forest were blackened tree stumps.

The firefighters began to search for their missing friends. After a few hours, they found twelve bodies. The dead had tried to outrun the fire. Days later, two more bodies were found.

By July 11, the Storm King fire was under control. But for 14 brave firefighters, it was too late. END

| Words to Know! | **metallic** | made of metal |

Comprehension Focus

Sequence of Events

▶ Complete this chart with the events that tell how the firefighters fought and survived the fire from "The Big Blowup" through the end of the article.

First

Then

After that

At last

The Key Idea

▶ **WRITE** What is this science text mostly about?

_____

_____

VOCABULARY
Target Word

abandon

a•ban•don (verb)

Rate It: ① ② ③ ④

Meaning

to leave _____

Example

People might have to

abandon _____

because of _____

_____

React and Write

▶ **WRITE** Would you evacuate your home during severe weather? Why or why not?

HURRICANES:
The Monster Storms

Hurricanes can be 600 miles across! When they hit land, it's a disaster!

Forces of Destruction

Hurricane Katrina was one of the worst storms ever to strike the United States. It hit in August 2005. Hurricane Floyd was another major storm. It hit the U.S. in September 1999.

Hurricanes bring intense wind and rain. These severe storms can flatten homes, schools, hospitals, and roads. Katrina's winds reached 175 miles an hour. It destroyed parts of Louisiana, Mississippi, Alabama, and Florida. Katrina killed nearly 2,000 people. Floyd dumped 20 inches of rain on North Carolina, causing record-breaking floods. It left 68 people dead.

Scientists often know when a brewing storm could become a danger. First, storm trackers fly planes into a storm at sea. Next, they measure its strength and size. If it looks bad, they warn people to evacuate the coast.

During Floyd, most people listened. They **abandoned** their homes. They found shelter far from the storm. Other people stayed—and got the scare of their lives.

Words to Know! **evacuate** to leave due to an emergency

Above, a satellite photo shows Hurricane Floyd as it approached Florida. Below, Kaleatha Vines survived the storm.

Refusing to Evacuate

Kaleatha Vines, 14, didn't evacuate before Floyd arrived. She and her family lived in Tarboro, North Carolina. They decided to withstand the storm. The local police pleaded with the Vineses to evacuate. Nothing could motivate them to leave. "It's not really going to flood," Kaleatha's father insisted.

Her father was wrong. Tarboro was one of the worst hit towns. The next morning, there was knee-deep water in their yard. The family knew they had to leave. They abandoned everything—even their dog!

Driving to the shelter, Kaleatha witnessed the storm's destruction. She saw cars hanging from trees. She saw animals rotting in the streets. The highway was covered with muddy floodwaters. Kaleatha was disgusted—and scared. Later, her house had to be rebuilt. Still, she is grateful. Why? She survived the deadly storm. ➤

 Sequence of Events

1. **UNDERLINE** When did Hurricane Katrina hit the United States?

2. ✔ **CHECK** Identify four signal words in "Forces of Destruction."

3. ▷ **WRITE** Number these events in the correct sequence from 1 (first) to 4 (last).

____ Scientists warned people to evacuate their homes.

____ Storm trackers measured the size and strength of the storms.

____ Storm trackers flew planes into the hurricanes.

____ People abandoned their homes to find shelter elsewhere.

 REVIEW
Main Idea and Details

CIRCLE Identify the main idea in "Refusing to Evacuate."

CRITICAL READING
Synthesize

▷ **WRITE** Imagine what it is like to see sections of your town destroyed, as Kaleatha did. Describe what you might see if a hurricane hit your town. Describe how you might feel.

_____

_____

_____

_____

_____

_____

Active Reading

CIRCLE How fast can a hurricane spin?

VOCABULARY
Target Word

cycle

cy•cle (noun)

Rate It: ① ② ③ ④

Meaning

a sequence of events that

_____

Example

The school year **cycle** begins in September and ends _____

_____

React and Write

▶ **WRITE** If a major storm was coming, who would you want to be there to help you? Why?

Summarize

▶ **WRITE** Summarize the topic and important details in the science text "Hurricanes: The Monster Storms."

How Hurricanes Are Born

A hurricane's life **cycle** begins over the ocean. First, warm, wet air starts to circle over the water. The winds spin slowly. They are spread out over a wide area. The center of the winds is called the eye. If the eye is tiny, tight, and round, a bad storm begins to form.

Then, the warm, moist air rises. The winds spin faster. Soon, wind and water swirl in a giant cloud over the ocean. When wind speed reaches 39 miles per hour, a tropical storm is born.

Next, a tropical storm can continue to grow. It just needs warm, wet air rising off the water. Water temperature must be above 81 degrees Fahrenheit. If it is cooler, the storm dies out.

Finally, a tropical storm can turn into a hurricane. How does that happen? When winds increase to 74 miles per hour, the storm becomes a hurricane. At its fastest, a hurricane can spin up to 200 miles per hour!

Words to Know!	**moist**	damp

📄 **TEXT FEATURE Reading a Diagram**

Inside a Hurricane

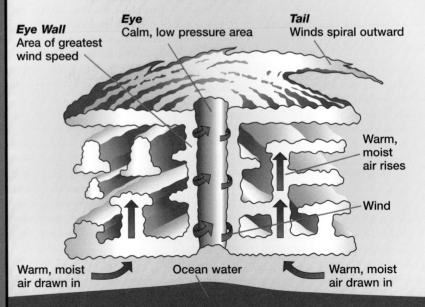

Eye Wall Area of greatest wind speed

Eye Calm, low pressure area

Tail Winds spiral outward

Warm, moist air rises

Wind

Warm, moist air drawn in

Ocean water

Warm, moist air drawn in

Hurricane Katrina caused major destruction that cost billions of dollars.

When Hurricanes Hit

What happens when a hurricane hits land? First, the front wall of the hurricane slams into the coast. It batters trees and houses with high winds. It dumps heavy rains onto the land. Next, the eye of the hurricane passes over. During this time, there is a lull in the storm. But then, the back wall of the hurricane arrives. The wind picks up strength again.

As a hurricane moves across land, it slowly loses its power. Winds slow down, especially after a storm crosses a mountain. Finally, after about ten days, the hurricane blows itself out. And then, the recovery can begin. *END*

A diagram shows you how a process works.

❶ What is the very center of the hurricane called?

Ⓐ the tail   Ⓑ the eye

Ⓒ the dome   Ⓓ the eye wall

❷ From where is warm, moist air drawn into the hurricane?

Ⓐ the top   Ⓑ the left

Ⓒ the bottom   Ⓓ the right

❸ **Synthesize:** Why does a hurricane have to begin at sea?

_____

_____

Sequence of Events

1. **UNDERLINE** Mark four signal words that tell the sequence of events in "How Hurricanes Are Born."

2. ▶ **WRITE** What happens after a tropical storm reaches 74 miles per hour?

_____

_____

CRITICAL READING
Synthesize

▶ **WRITE** A hurricane has immense power. Complete this sentence to describe the force of a hurricane.

A hurricane is as strong as

_____

_____

✓ Skills Check

1. **CIRCLE** Identify seven sequence words and phrases in "When Hurricanes Hit."

2. ▶ **WRITE** Number these steps in the correct sequence from 1 (first) to 4 (last).

____ The hurricane blows itself out.

____ The front wall of the hurricane hits land.

____ The eye of the hurricane passes over.

____ The hurricane slows down over land.

Word Challenge

start ┈┈┈

3 Prefixes

1 **Rate them.** Which causes the most **severe destruction** in your state? Which causes the least?

1 = least **severe**
4 = most **severe**

____ floods

____ fires

____ tornadoes

____ earthquakes

A **prefix** is a letter or a group of letters added to the beginning of a word. A prefix changes the meaning of a word. The prefix *re-* means "again." *Reread* means "to read again." The prefix *un-* means "not." *Unspoken* means "not spoken."

Guess the meaning of each word, using your knowledge of these prefixes.

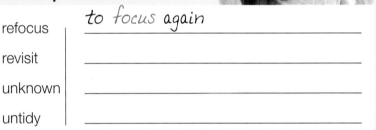

*I love this song! I've already **replayed** it 100 times.*

refocus	*to focus again*
revisit	_____
unknown	_____
untidy	_____

2 **Use this scale.** You can **prevent**:

	yes	maybe	never
a hurricane.	☐	☐	☐
a pimple.	☐	☐	☐
a fistfight.	☐	☐	☐
a cold.	☐	☐	☐

4 **Check two.** Which two weather forecasts sound the worst to you?

☐ "Winds tomorrow will exceed 10 mph."

☐ "Tomorrow's temperature will exceed 110 **degrees**."

☐ "Tomorrow's snowfall will exceed four inches."

☐ "A new storm **cycle** will begin tomorrow with strong winds."

5 **List.** Look at the list of events below. Write a personal example for each. Be ready to explain what made each **major** for you.

a **major** birthday: _____

a **major** embarrassment: _____

a **major** scare: _____

8 Suffixes

A **suffix** is a letter or group of letters added to the end of a word. A suffix changes the meaning or part of speech of a word. The suffixes *-ion,-tion,* and *-ation* turn verbs into nouns. So, *evacuate* is a verb. *Evacuation* is a noun.

Turn these verbs into nouns by adding *-ion, -tion,* **or** *-ation.*

prevent: _____

construct: _____

determine: _____

adore: _____

construct + ion = construction

6 **Analyze.** Who causes accidents on the road? Put *A* for agree and *D* for disagree.

____ Mothers **increase** the risk of accidents.

____ Teen drivers **increase** the risk of accidents.

____ Sleepy drivers **increase** the risk of accidents.

____ Teachers **increase** the risk of accidents.

9 **Evaluate.** True or false, the best way to eat a worm is to chew it slowly and **focus** on how it tastes.

True   False

Why? _____

_____

_____

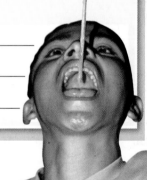

7 **Complete.** If I had to evacuate my home, . . .

I might **abandon**:

_____

I would definitely **abandon**:

_____

I would never **abandon**:

_____

10 **Rate.** How long would your **recovery** be if you . . .

saw a scary movie? _____

had a fight with a friend? _____

broke a leg? _____

 finish

Writing Text Type
Narrative Paragraph

A **narrative paragraph** tells a story about a real or imagined event or experience.

▶ **Read Jaydon Washington's narrative paragraph about a disaster in his town.**

Introductory Statement

An **introductory statement** identifies the topic of the narrative and establishes a point of view.

1. **UNDERLINE** the introductory statement.

Detail Sentences

Detail sentences describe events in **time order**.

2. **NUMBER** the events 1–5 in time order.

Sensory details bring the setting, events, and people or characters to life for readers.

3. ✔ **CHECK** five sensory details.

Language Use

Transition words and phrases connect details.

4. **CIRCLE** five transition words and phrases.

The writer uses **vivid adjectives** to describe the experience in a lively way.

5. **DOUBLE UNDERLINE** four vivid adjectives.

Concluding Sentence

The **concluding sentence** completes the narrative in a satisfying way.

6. ★ **STAR** the concluding sentence.

Student Model

The Terrible Tornado
by Jaydon Washington

When I was 8, a fierce tornado nearly destroyed my hometown of Cincinnati, Ohio. At first, my younger brother and I thought it was going to be a rainstorm. Dark, gray clouds blocked out the sun, and we heard a terrible rumble. Then, the sky turned a frightening yellow-gray. Soon, chunks of hail the size of softballs began pounding on our roof. The violent wind hollered and shook the trees. My mother rushed us into the basement, and we hid there for over an hour. Later that evening, the news reported that the severe storm that passed over our area was actually a tornado! The next day, we saw the destruction the tornado caused. Cracked branches and garbage cans were everywhere. We realized how lucky we were!

Brainstorm

► Read the writing prompt in the middle of the idea web.
  Then use the boxes to help you brainstorm ideas.

Coldest Weather

Hottest Weather

Writing Prompt:
Tell about a time when you experienced severe weather.

Wettest Weather

Wildest Weather

Choose Your Topic

► Select one of your ideas from the idea web. Then complete the sentences below.

I plan to write about _____

The weather was so severe that _____

Organize Ideas for Writing

▶ **Complete this outline with notes for your narrative paragraph.**

I. Introductory Statement. Identify the topic of your narrative.

Topic: _____

Point of View: _____

II. Detail Sentences. List two sensory details about the event or experience.

Detail 1: _____

Detail 2: _____

III. Concluding Sentence. Sum up the narrative in a satisfying way.

_____

_____

Write Your Draft

▶ **Write a draft of your narrative paragraph.**

Writing Prompt:
Tell about a time when you experienced severe weather.

WORD CHOICES	
Everyday	**Precise**
mess	destruction
said	reported
big	major

_____
(narrative title)

▶ **Write your introductory statement.**

Introductory Statement

The most severe weather I experienced was _____
(topic and point of view)

_____.

▶ **Type your introductory statement on the computer or write it on paper. Then use these transition words and phrases to complete a draft of your paragraph.**

Detail Sentences

First, . . .	*Then, . . .*
After a while, . . .	*The next day, . . .*

Concluding Sentence

I/We felt . . .	*I/We thought . . .*

Revise Your Paragraph

▶ **Evaluate:** Rate your paragraph. Then have a writing partner rate it.

Scoring Guide			
needs improvement	average	good	excellent
1	2	3	4

1. **UNDERLINE** the introductory statement. Does it identify the topic?
   Self   1   2   3   4
   Partner   1   2   3   4

2. **NUMBER** the events 1–5. Are they in time order?
   Self   1   2   3   4
   Partner   1   2   3   4

3. ✔**CHECK** the sensory details. Do they bring the story to life for readers?
   Self   1   2   3   4
   Partner   1   2   3   4

4. ⬭**CIRCLE** the transition words and phrases. Do they connect ideas?
   Self   1   2   3   4
   Partner   1   2   3   4

5. **DOUBLE UNDERLINE** the adjectives. Are they vivid?
   Self   1   2   3   4
   Partner   1   2   3   4

6. ★**STAR** the concluding sentence. Does it sum up the narrative in a satisfying way?
   Self   1   2   3   4
   Partner   1   2   3   4

▶ **Discuss:** Give feedback on your partner's narrative paragraph.

1. Start with positive comments about your partner's narrative paragraph.

   You did an effective job of _____
   _____

   The experience you described was _____
   _____

2. Give your partner suggestions for revision.

   I have a question about _____
   _____

   Your detail sentences _____
   _____

   The narrative paragraph needs _____
   _____

3. Answer any questions your partner has about your suggestions.

4. Ask your partner for feedback. Use the frames below to summarize your partner's feedback.

   You appreciated the way I . . .
   You had a question about . . .
   You suggested that . . .
   My paragraph needs . . .

▶ **Revise** Now revise your narrative paragraph.

Grammar CORRECTING SENTENCE FRAGMENTS

A **sentence fragment** is an incomplete sentence. Often, sentence fragments are missing a subject or a verb. To correct some fragments, add a subject or verb to make a **complete sentence**.

Example

Sentence Fragment	Complete Sentence
A tornado our town today. [missing verb]	A tornado **struck** our town today.
Brought the trees down. [missing subject]	**A storm** brought the trees down.

▶ **Write whether each fragment below is missing a subject or a verb.**

1. The wind outside against the trees. _____ *verb*

2. Beat my window and kept me awake all night. _____

3. Some trees from the park on Main Street. _____

4. Finally, after the wind died down, went outside. _____

5. The next day, only some clouds. _____

To correct some **sentence fragments**, you can connect the fragment to a complete sentence by adding a comma and any missing words.

Example

Sentence and Fragment	Complete Sentence
A tornado struck our town today. Touched down in Texas. [missing subject]	A tornado struck our town today, **and then it** touched down in Texas.

▶ **Rewrite each sentence and fragment as one complete sentence.**

6. We studied storms in class. Including tornadoes.

_____

7. Storms are fun to study. Not to experience yourself.

_____

8. Our teacher led an experiment. Then a quiz.

_____

9. We all expected a test. But not until Friday.

_____

▶ **Edit Your Draft.** Take a close look at each sentence in your draft. **Does each sentence express a complete thought?** Fix the ones that do not.

Mechanics USING CAPITAL LETTERS

Some words begin with a **capital letter**.

- The first word in a sentence always begins with a capital letter.
- A proper noun always begins with a capital letter.

Example

Correct	Incorrect
Lightning struck the building.	lightning struck the building.
The storm flooded Emily's home.	The storm flooded emily's home.

▶ **Find and correct five errors in this paragraph.**

Student Model

> When my brother ralph was a baby, our house was flooded. That spring, it rained every day. Soon, the river began to rise. one day, water covered the road. A boat carried us to saftey, but the river kept rising. Finally, we went back to our house. Mud on the walls two feet high. For weeks, the house smelled bad. The flood caused lots of destrucktion!

CHECK AND CORRECT

- ☐ Correct one sentence fragment.
- ☐ <u>UNDERLINE</u> two capitalization errors and correct them.
- ☐ (CIRCLE) two spelling errors and correct them.

▶ **Edit Your Draft.** Look at the sentences in your own draft. **Does each sentence use capital letters correctly?** Fix the ones that do not.

Final Draft/Present

▶ **Write a final draft of your paragraph on the computer or on paper. Check it again and correct any errors before you present it.**

Focus Skill | Gather Information

Use a Weather Map

Severe storms or pleasant sunshine? Use a weather map to know the temperature and conditions outside.

▶ **Read this weather map of the mainland United States. Then, answer the questions below about gathering information.**

MARK IT

- **UNDERLINE** the city with the warmest sunny weather.
- CIRCLE two areas where thunderstorms are reported.
- ★**STAR** the city with the coolest temperatures.

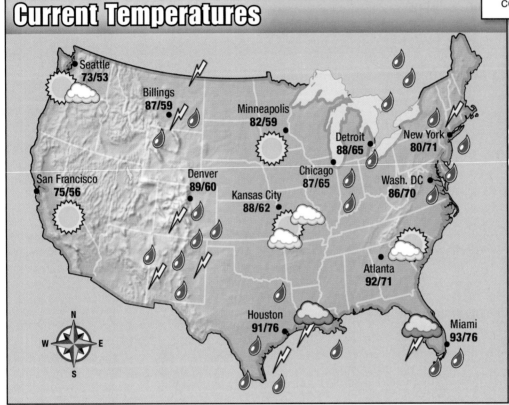

Current Temperatures

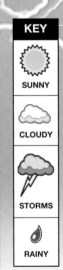

KEY

SUNNY
CLOUDY
STORMS
RAINY

---

① **Where are the most storms?**

  Ⓐ San Francisco

  Ⓑ in the East

  Ⓒ in the South

  Ⓓ Chicago

② **Who might find this weather map useful?**

  Ⓐ a U.S. airline pilot

  Ⓑ a bus driver in Colorado

  Ⓒ a TV weather reporter

  Ⓓ all of the above

③ **Based on this weather map, would you rather be in Miami or Minneapolis? Explain.**

_____

_____

_____

_____

_____

_____

_____

Storm Tracker
Robin Tanamachi

This scientist tracks tornadoes to see how they form.

▶ **Read the work schedule and job information. Then answer the questions below about Robin Tanamachi's job.**

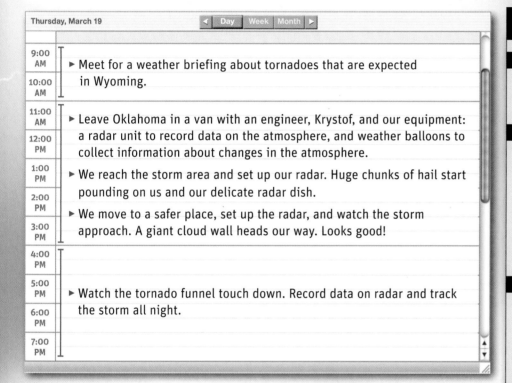

Thursday, March 19   ◀ Day | Week | Month ▶

- **9:00 AM – 10:00 AM** ▶ Meet for a weather briefing about tornadoes that are expected in Wyoming.

- **11:00 AM – 12:00 PM** ▶ Leave Oklahoma in a van with an engineer, Krystof, and our equipment: a radar unit to record data on the atmosphere, and weather balloons to collect information about changes in the atmosphere.

- **1:00 PM** ▶ We reach the storm area and set up our radar. Huge chunks of hail start pounding on us and our delicate radar dish.

- **2:00 PM – 3:00 PM** ▶ We move to a safer place, set up the radar, and watch the storm approach. A giant cloud wall heads our way. Looks good!

- **5:00 PM – 6:00 PM** ▶ Watch the tornado funnel touch down. Record data on radar and track the storm all night.

ON THE JOB

EDUCATION

Bachelor's degree in Meteorology

RESPONSIBILITIES
- Records data on size, location, and other tornado details
- Analyzes data after each tornado-tracking mission
- Sets up, operates, and maintains technical equipment

SKILLS
- Working with a team
- Communicating data clearly to team leaders
- Operating scientific tools

SALARY

$29,000–$50,000

FAVORITE PART OF WORK

"I love being the first person to see new data. It makes me feel like an explorer!"

CAREER CONNECTION

Science, Technology, Engineering, and Mathematics
www.careerclusters.org

Related Jobs
- meteorologist
- science teacher
- science museum guide

❶ What tools do Robin Tanamachi and the other scientists use to gather information about tornadoes?

_____

_____

❷ How risky do you think Tanamachi's job is? Mark the line.

  1   2   3   4   5

Not very risky   **Very risky**

❸ I think Tanamachi's job is/is not (circle one) risky because

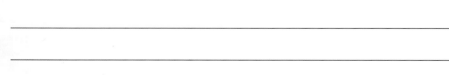

_____

_____

What is your disaster plan?

A natural disaster could happen at any time. How would you respond if a major storm or earthquake hit while you were in school? Propose a plan for what to do if a disaster strikes.

❶ Brainstorm risks. List two possible disasters that could hit your area.

A. _____

B. _____

❷ Ask questions. What questions might people have during an emergency? Consider the different groups at your school that would be affected.

Groups Affected	Questions
Teachers and School Officials	• What's the best way to communicate the plan in the school building?
Students	
Parents	

❸ Collaborate. Decide what would need to happen during a disaster. Add five more actions to the web. Then, circle the three best actions for students to take.

Follow instructions carefully.

What needs to be done?

④ **Prepare your plan.** Create a brochure or poster describing three actions students at your school should take in response to a disaster. Include or describe images for your brochure.

Title: _____

Introduction: _____

_____

_____

ACTION 1: _Follow instructions carefully._

Why it is important: _This is important because we would hear important announcements about what to do and where to go to stay safe._

_____

ACTION 2: _____

Why it is important: _This is important because_ _____

_____

_____

ACTION 3: _____

Why it is important: _This is important because_ _____

_____

Caption: _____   **Caption:** _____

Comprehension

▶ **Fill in the circle next to the correct answer.**

1. After Justin was hit by lightning, what was his most serious long-term problem?

Ⓐ seizures

Ⓑ unconsciousness

Ⓒ memory lapses

Ⓓ fear of thunderstorms

> **Here's a Tip.**
> For fill-in-the-blank questions, substitute each answer for the blank in the sentence. Then pick the best one.

2. More firefighters on the scene would have made the Storm King fire _____.

Ⓐ increase in intensity

Ⓑ less deadly

Ⓒ spread to nearby mountains

Ⓓ difficult to battle

CRITICAL READING

3. Synthesize: What kind of destruction does a wildfire cause?

Ⓐ It shakes the ground under houses and destroys them.

Ⓑ It blows houses over and causes floods.

Ⓒ It strikes people at their jobs and knocks them unconscious.

Ⓓ It spreads deadly flames that destroy homes and forests.

4. When a hurricane is coming, experts usually tell people who live near the coast to _____.

Ⓐ stay at home

Ⓑ evacuate their homes

Ⓒ go to a boat to stay safe

Ⓓ get into small, heat-resistant shelters

CRITICAL READING

5. Synthesize: A hurricane is most likely to happen _____.

Ⓐ on tall mountains

Ⓑ near an ocean

Ⓒ in forests

Ⓓ at the Earth's poles

Vocabulary

▶ **Fill in the circle next to the correct definition of the underlined word.**

1. Hurricane Floyd caused <u>major</u> flooding in many areas of the South.
   - Ⓐ very small or unimportant
   - Ⓒ very large or important
   - Ⓑ frightening
   - Ⓓ deep and cold

2. After being struck by lightning, Justin had a long <u>recovery</u> period.
   - Ⓐ the process of getting better
   - Ⓒ uncomfortable
   - Ⓑ hospitalized
   - Ⓓ disturbing

3. If you hear a <u>severe</u> storm warning on the news, you wait for more information.
   - Ⓐ very fun and amusing
   - Ⓒ very scary or exciting
   - Ⓑ very wet and windy
   - Ⓓ very bad or serious

▶ **What does the prefix in the underlined word mean?**

4. If you <u>recycle</u> newspapers, fewer trees have to be cut down for paper.
   - Ⓐ not
   - Ⓒ extra
   - Ⓑ again
   - Ⓓ back

▶ **Fill in the circle next to the words that best complete the sentence.**

5. Educating people about fire _____ can stop the _____ of forests.
   - Ⓐ prevent, destroy
   - Ⓒ prevented, destroyed
   - Ⓑ prevention, destruction
   - Ⓓ preventer, destroyer

Short Answer

CRITICAL READING ▶ **Synthesize:** Use what you've read in this Workshop to answer the question below. Check your spelling and grammar.

What do you think should be done at the first sign of a natural disaster?

_____

_____

_____

_____

_____

WORKSHOP 3

COMPREHENSION FOCUS
Story Elements

CRITICAL READING FOCUS
Evaluate

Literary Text

Reading 1 Louisa, Please Come Home |
Short Story

Reading 2 I'm Nobody! Who are you? | **Poetry**

Reading 3 A Whole New Look | **Poetry**

Identity Crisis

Have you ever felt like people don't really know you? Shirley Jackson asks this question in her story "Louisa, Please Come Home." Jackson is best known for writing strange tales with twist endings.

In this story, Louisa decides to run away from home. Find out what happens when she tries to return.

Academic Vocabulary

Target Word	Meaning	Examples
◎ **Target Word** ▶ Read the Target Words. Rate each one using the scale below.*	▶ Read the Target Word meanings. Write in the missing words.	▶ Finish the Target Word examples below.
unique (p. 66) u•nique (adjective) ① ② ③ ④	_____ and one-of-a-kind	I dyed my hair so I would look **unique**.
recognize (p. 68) rec•og•nize (verb) ① ② ③ ④	to _____ or hear someone and _____ who the person is	• If you tried to trick me on the phone, I would **recognize** _____ _____ • A person might **recognize** me by my _____
identity (p. 68) i•den•ti•ty (noun) ① ② ③ ④	who a person is	• An important part of my **identity** is _____ • A criminal can try to steal your **identity** by _____ _____
secure (p. 69) se•cure (adjective) ① ② ③ ④	safe and not likely to be at _____	• Her role as team captain is **secure** because _____ _____ • We check _____ to make sure they are **secure**.
deceive (p. 72) de•ceive (verb) ① ② ③ ④	to trick	• A person who might try to **deceive** you is _____ _____ • I would never **deceive** _____ _____

***Rating Scale**
① = I don't know the word. ③ = I think I know the word.
② = I've seen it or heard it. ④ = I know it and use it.

Comprehension Focus
Story Elements

A **short story** like "Louisa, Please Come Home" is a brief work of fiction. To understand a short story, pay attention to four elements:

1. Setting is where and when the story takes place. This story takes place in a city during the 1950s.

2. Characters are the people in the story.

| **Louisa Tether,** a 19-year-old girl | **Mr. and Mrs. Tether and Carol,** Louisa's family | **Paul,** Louisa's neighbor | **Mrs. Peacock,** owner of a rooming house |

3. Plot is the sequence of events in a story. The plot contains a problem that the main character needs to solve. In "Louisa, Please Come Home," the main character runs away from home. She faces a major challenge when she decides to return.

4. Theme is an important message about life that the author wants readers to understand. A story can have more than one theme. One theme of this story is: People often don't fully appreciate what they have until they have lost it.

▶ **Turn the page to begin reading Louisa's story.**

Louisa, Please Come Home

▶ **Complete this chart as you reread the story.**

	Part 1 (pp. 64–65)	Part 2 (pp. 66–69)	Part 3 (pp. 70–73)
Setting	Time: June 20, in the 1950s Place: a city called Chandler	Time: Place:	Time: Place:
Character	Who is the main character? Describe him/her:	How does the character change?	What is the character like now?
Plot Events	What happens at the beginning of the story?	What happens in the middle of the story?	How does the story end?
Theme	Author's message:		

Active Reading

★**STAR** When Louisa leaves home, what is her family in the middle of preparing for?

VOCABULARY
Target Word

error

er•ror (noun)

Rate It: ① ② ③ ④

Meaning

a _____

Example

An **error** I often make is

_____

Craft and Structure

Point of View is the perspective a story is told from. The first-person point of view uses the pronoun *I* or *we*. The third-person point of view uses the pronoun *he*, *she*, or *they*.

▶ **WRITE** What is the point of view in "Louisa, Please Come Home"?

_____

React and Write

▶ **WRITE** Why might someone run away from home?

_____

Louisa, Please Come Home

adapted from the story by **Shirley Jackson**

I listened to my mother's trembling voice over the radio. "Louisa," she said, "please come home. It's been three years since we saw you. We all miss you, and we want you back again. Louisa, please come home."

Once a year I heard that announcement on the anniversary of the day I ran away. I also read the newspaper stories about myself. "Louisa Tether disappeared one year ago." Or two years, or three. I used to wait for June 20 as if it were my birthday.

I was residing in Chandler. It was a big enough city for me to hide in. It was also near my old home, so the papers always made a big fuss about the anniversary of my disappearance.

I didn't decide to leave home on the spur of the moment. I had been planning it for a long time.

Words to Know!	**residing**	living in a particular place

I knew that everything had to go just right because if I made any **errors**, I would have looked like a ridiculous fool. My sister Carol would never have let me forget that.

I admit I planned my departure for the day before Carol's wedding. The newspapers reported that my family had the wedding anyway. Carol told a reporter that her sister Louisa would have wanted it that way.

"She would never have wanted to spoil my wedding," Carol explained. But secretly, she knew that was exactly what I'd wanted.

Anyway, on that day, everyone was hurrying around the house, making preparations for the wedding. I just walked out the door and started my new life. ➤

 Story Elements

Setting

1. CIRCLE What sentence or phrase tells you about the city of Chandler, where Louisa is living?

Character

2. UNDERLINE What does Louisa's sister Carol say about her wedding?

3. ▶ WRITE What does this detail tell you about Carol and her feelings toward Louisa?

_____

_____

_____

Plot

4. ▶ WRITE What does Louisa's family do the day after she runs away from home?

_____

_____

_____

Theme

5. ★STAR One theme of this story is: "People often don't appreciate what they have until they have lost it." What detail in the story shows that Louisa did not appreciate her home and family?

▶ **Now go to page 63. Add details to Part 1 of the chart.**

Active Reading

★**STAR** Who does Louisa decide she is going to be?

VOCABULARY
Target Word

genuinely

gen•u•ine•ly (adverb)

Rate It: ① ② ③ ④

Meaning

_____ or sincerely

Example

You can tell when people genuinely like you by

_____

CRITICAL READING
Evaluate

1. ✔**CHECK** Does Mrs. Peacock genuinely like Louisa?

   ❏ yes   ❏ no

2. ✔**CHECK** Mark one detail that supports your response.

React and Write

▶**WRITE** How well do you pay attention to the people around you? Do you think you would have noticed Louisa?

There was only one bad minute when Paul saw me. Paul lived next door to us, and Carol hates him more than she hates me. My mother can't stand him, either.

Of course, Paul didn't know I was running away. I told him the exact same story I had told my parents. I was going downtown to get away from all the confusion and excitement. Paul wanted to come with me, but I ran for the bus and left him standing there.

I rode the bus downtown and then walked to the railroad station. I purchased a round-trip ticket to Crain to make them think I was planning to return. That way they wouldn't start looking for me too quickly.

I knew they'd think I would stay in Crain. It was the biggest city the train went to. But my plan was to stay there for only part of one day.

To change my appearance, I bought a tan raincoat in a department store in Crain. I had left home wearing a conspicuous new jacket. I just left the jacket on a counter in the store. Someone probably bought it.

I was pretty confident about one thing: There must be thousands of 19-year-old girls, fair-haired, five feet four inches tall, weighing 126 pounds. And a lot of them would be wearing shapeless tan raincoats. I wouldn't be unique, and nobody would detect me.

It's funny how no one pays any attention to you. Hundreds of people saw me that day, but no one really saw me.

I took a train to Chandler, which is the place where I'd been heading all along. I slept on the train.

When I got there, I bought a suitcase, stockings, and a little clock. I put the other items in the suitcase. Then I was ready to get settled in Chandler. Nothing is hard to do unless you get upset or excited about it.

Words to Know! **conspicuous** very easy to notice

Literature

L

I decided what my new identity would be. I was a 19-year-old girl named Lois Taylor who had a nice family upstate. I had saved enough money to come live in Chandler. When the summer ended, I would go to business school. I would need a job to pay for it.

I stopped in a drugstore for breakfast and a paper. I read the ads for furnished rooms. Everything about me appeared so normal—suitcase, raincoat, rooms for rent. When I asked the clerk at the drugstore how to get to Primrose Street, he never even glanced at me.

I walked into Mrs. Peacock's house on Primrose Street, and right away, I knew this was the perfect place. My room was nice, and Mrs. Peacock and I **genuinely** liked each other.

She was pleased that my mother wanted me to find a clean room in a good neighborhood. And she was even more pleased that I wanted to save money so I could send some home every week.➤

Story Elements

Setting

1. (CIRCLE) What two cities does Louisa go to?

2. ▣▷ **WRITE** In what city does she stay?

_____

Character

3. ▣▷ **WRITE** How would you describe Louisa's personality?

_____

_____

Plot

4. ▣▷ **WRITE** What important events happen in this part of the story?

_____

_____

_____

_____

Theme

5. **UNDERLINE** A theme of this story is: "Though people might know you, they don't always see the real you." Mark a detail that supports this theme.

Identity Crisis (67)

Active Reading

WRITE What is one thing Louisa tells Mrs. Peacock about her family?

_____

_____

VOCABULARY
Target Word

respond

re•spond (verb)

Rate It: ① ② ③ ④

Meaning

to _____ to something that has been said or done

Example

You should **respond** immediately to _____

_____

React and Write

WRITE Is it believable that Louisa was able to change her identity so easily? Why or why not?

Within an hour, Mrs. Peacock knew all the details about my imaginary family. I told her that my mother was a widow, my sister had just been married, and my younger brother Paul made my mother worry a lot because he didn't want to settle down.

Mrs. Peacock was eager to take care of me. She told me about a job in a stationery store. So there I was. I had been away from home for 24 hours, and already I was a whole new person. I was Lois Taylor. I lived on Primrose Street and worked at the stationery store.

In the mornings, Mrs. Peacock and I would read the newspapers during breakfast. She'd ask my opinion about the girl who disappeared over in Rockville. I'd say she must be insane to leave a nice home like that.

Once I picked up the newspaper and looked intently at the picture. "Do you think she looks like me?" I asked Mrs. Peacock.

"No," Mrs. Peacock **responded**. "Her hair is longer, and her face is fatter than yours."

"I think she kind of resembles me," I said.

My picture appeared in the Chandler papers a lot, but no one ever looked at me twice. I went to work, I shopped in the stores, and I went to the movies and the beach with Mrs. Peacock. Still, no one recognized me. I had done a perfect job of changing my identity.

One morning, Mrs. Peacock was reading about my disappearance. "They're saying now that she was kidnapped," she said.

"I feel kind of sorry for her," I said.

"You can never tell," she said. "Maybe she went willingly with the kidnapper."

On the anniversary of my running away, I bought a new hat. When I got home, Mrs. Peacock was listening to the radio. I heard my mother's familiar voice.

"Louisa," she said, "please come home."

"That poor woman," Mrs. Peacock said. "Imagine how she must feel. She hasn't given up hope of finding her little girl alive some day."

I decided not to go to business school after all, since the stationery store was expanding, and I would probably be a manager soon. Mrs. Peacock and I agreed it would be foolish to give up such a secure job.

By this time, I had some savings in the bank. I was adjusting to my new life. I never had a thought about returning home. It was just plain bad luck that I had an encounter with Paul. ➤

Words to Know!	**expanding** getting bigger

Story Elements

Setting

1. ▷ **WRITE** When do Louisa and Mrs. Peacock read the newspaper together?

_____

_____

Character

2. **UNDERLINE** Mark two sentences or phrases that tell how Louisa feels about her new life.

Plot

3. ▷ **WRITE** What happens on Louisa's anniversary of running away?

_____

_____

_____

_____

Theme

4. (CIRCLE) A theme of this story is: "Though people might know you, they don't always see the real you." Identify a paragraph that supports this theme.

▶ Now go to page 63. Add details to Part 2 of the chart.

Read for Detail

▷ **WRITE** What does Louisa buy for herself on the anniversary of the day she ran away?

_____

Active Reading

★**STAR** What threat does Paul make to Louisa?

 VOCABULARY
Target Word

precisely

pre•cise•ly *(adverb)*

Rate It: ① ② ③ ④

Meaning

_____

_____

Example

_____

must be followed **precisely.**

 CRITICAL READING
Evaluate

▶ **WRITE** Do you think it was a good idea for Louisa to go home? Why or why not?

_____

_____

_____

_____

_____

_____

 React and Write

▶ **WRITE** Describe a time you reunited with someone you had not seen for a long time. How did the person react?

I didn't stop to think when I recognized him on the street. I automatically yelled, "Paul!"

He turned around and stared at me with a shocked expression on his face. Then he said, "Is it possible?"

He said I had to go back. If I didn't, he threatened to tell my parents where I was. He told me there was still a reward for anyone who found me, and assured me that I could run away again after he got the reward.

Maybe I really wanted to go home; maybe that's why I yelled his name out on the street. Anyway, I decided to go with him.

I told Mrs. Peacock that I was leaving to visit my family upstate. I thought that was funny. Paul sent a telegram to my mother and father.

Words to Know! | **assured** promised

When we arrived in Rockville, we took a taxi to my house. I began to get nervous as I looked out the window. I would have sworn that I hadn't thought about Rockville for three years, but I remembered it all **precisely**, as if I had never been away.

The taxi turned onto my street. When I saw the house, I almost cried. "Everything looks just the same," I said. "I caught the bus right there on the corner."

"If I had managed to stop you that day," Paul said, "you would probably never have tried again."

As we walked up the driveway, I wondered if my family was watching from the window, and if I'd have to ring the doorbell. I'd never had to ring it before.

I was still wondering when Carol opened the door. "Carol!" I said. I was genuinely glad to see her.

Carol looked at me hard, then she stepped back and I saw my mother and father. I was going to run to them, but I held myself back. I wasn't sure if they were angry with me, or hurt, or happy that I was back.

I wasn't sure of what to say, so I just stood there and said, "Mother?" kind of uncertainly.

She put her hands on my shoulders, and then looked at my face for a long time. There were tears running down her cheeks, and she looked old and sad.

Then she turned to Paul and said, "Oh Paul, how could you do this to me again?"

Paul looked frightened. "Mrs. Tether—"

My mother asked me, "What is your name, dear?"

"Louisa Tether," I said stupidly.

"No, dear," she said very gently. "Your real name."

Now I felt like crying. "Louisa Tether," I said. "That's my name." ➤

Story Elements

Setting

1. ▶ **WRITE** How does the setting in this part of the story change?

_____

_____

_____

_____

Character

2. **UNDERLINE** How does Louisa feel about her sister Carol when she sees her?

Plot

3. ▶ **WRITE** What problem does Louisa have when she sees her family?

_____

_____

_____

_____

Theme

4. (CIRCLE) How does Louisa react when she sees her house?

5. ✔ **CHECK** Which theme best fits this part of the story?

❏ A mother always knows her own child best.

❏ People often appreciate something more after they've lost it.

❏ Your neighbors are always there to help you.

Active Reading

▶ **WRITE** How has Paul tried to deceive the Tether family?

_____

_____

_____

_____

VOCABULARY
Target Word

evident

ev•i•dent *(adjective)*

Rate It: ① ② ③ ④

Meaning

easily _____

or understood

Example

*It was **evident** from the look on her face that she was* _____ *about the news.*

React and Write

▶ **WRITE** Do you like the story's ending? Why or why not?

Make Inferences

Why does Louisa correct herself and call her father "Mr. Tether" instead of calling him "my father"?

"Why don't you people leave us alone?" Carol screamed. "We've spent years trying to find my sister. And people like you just try to cheat us out of the reward money—and we get hurt and heartbroken all over again."

"Carol," my father said, "you're frightening the poor child. Young lady," he said to me, "I don't think you realize the cruelty of what you are doing. You look like a nice girl. Try to imagine how your own mother would feel if someone did this to her."

I tried to imagine my own mother. I looked straight at her.

My father said, "I'm sure this young man didn't tell you he's taken advantage of us before. He's tried to deceive us twice when he's brought us girls who pretended to be our Louisa. The first time we were fooled for several days. The girl looked like our Louisa, and she acted like our Louisa. She even knew about personal family things that only Louisa—or Paul—could know. But she was not our daughter. She was an impostor. And my wife suffers more each time her hopes are raised."

He put one arm around my mother and the other around Carol. They all stood there staring at me.

Paul started to argue with them. I suddenly realized that all I wanted was to stay here, but it was **evident** that I couldn't. They had made up their minds that I wasn't Louisa.

"Paul," I said, "can't you see that you're only making Mr. Tether angry?"

"Correct, young lady," my father said.

"Paul," I said, "these people don't want us here."

Words to Know!	**impostor** someone who pretends to be someone else

Paul was about to argue again, but instead, he turned and stomped off toward the door.

I turned to follow him. My father—I mean Mr. Tether—came up behind me and took my hand. "My daughter was younger than you," he said in a gentle tone. "But I'm certain you have a family somewhere. Go back to the people who love you."

That meant Mrs. Peacock, I guess.

"To make sure you get there," my father said, "I want you to take this." He put a folded bill in my hand. "I hope someone will do as much for our Louisa."

"Good-bye, my dear," my mother said, and reached up and patted my cheek. "Good luck to you."

"I hope your daughter comes back some day," I told them. "Good-bye."

The bill was a twenty, and I gave it to Paul. He'd gone to a lot of trouble, and I still had my job at the stationery store.

My mother still talks to me on the radio, once a year, on the anniversary of the day I ran away.

"Louisa," she says, "please come home. We all want our dear girl back, and we need you and miss you so much. Your mother and father love you and will never forget you. Louisa, please come home." END

Meet the Author

SHIRLEY JACKSON
Born: 1916 in San Francisco, California

Writing Career: At age 12, Jackson won her first poetry contest. In high school, she kept a diary of her short stories. By the time she was in college, Jackson would write a thousand words every day.

Famous Works: Her famous stories include "The Lottery" and "Charles."

Words to Know!	**tone** a way of speaking that shows a certain feeling

 Story Elements

Setting

1. ▮▷ **WRITE** Where is Louisa living at the end of the story?

_____

_____

Character

2. ▮▷ **WRITE** What words would you use to describe Paul?

_____

Theme

3. (CIRCLE) What detail on page 72 shows Louisa's real feelings about home and her family?

▶ **Now go to page 63. Complete Part 3 of the chart and the theme.**

✓ **Skills Check**

1. ▮▷ **WRITE** What new problem does Louisa have?

_____

_____

_____

2. ▮▷ **WRITE** How have Louisa's feelings about her family changed?

_____

_____

_____

Active Reading

▶ **WRITE** What happens when the speaker of the second poem goes to school on Friday?

_____

_____

Craft and Structure

Rhyme Two or more words rhyme when their ending syllables have the same or similar sounds.

1. (CIRCLE) What words rhyme in "I'm Nobody! Who are you?"

A **simile** compares two unlike things, using the words _like_ or _as_.

2. UNDERLINE What is the simile in "I'm Nobody! Who are you?"

CRITICAL READING
Evaluate

▶ **WRITE** Does the speaker in "A Whole New Look" feel confident about her identity? Explain.

_____

_____

_____

React and Write

▶ **WRITE** Which poem do you like more? Why?

I'm Nobody! Who are you?

by Emily Dickinson

I'm Nobody! Who are you?
Are you—Nobody—too?
Then there's a pair of us!
Don't tell! they'd advertise—
    you know!

How dreary—to be—Somebody!
How public—like a Frog—
To tell one's name—
the livelong June—
To an admiring Bog!

A Whole New Look

by Angela Shelf Medearis

I got my braces taken off on Tuesday.

I got my hair cut and a curly perm on Wednesday.

I got contacts on Thursday.

Friday when I went to school

no one knew who I was.

Craft and Structure

Text Structure A stanza is a group of two or more lines in a poem. One idea or topic often connects the lines in a stanza.

1. **CIRCLE** each stanza in "I'm Nobody! Who are you?"

2. ▶ **WRITE** What event is the topic of the first stanza?

_____

_____

_____

A poem's **speaker or persona** is a character that the poet creates to tell the story. The speaker's voice is often different from the poet's voice.

3. ✔ **CHECK** What is the most likely age of the speaker in "A Whole New Look"?

❑ age 3
❑ age 13
❑ age 63

4. ★ **STAR** Mark two details in the poem that support your response.

Theme is an important message about life that the author wants readers to understand.

5. ▶ **WRITE** What message do these poems share with "Louisa, Please Come Home"?

_____

_____

_____

WORD CHALLENGE

I **listen** to a ton of music! Yesterday, I **listened** to my music for eight hours nonstop!

START

1 **Think about it.** If you won a million dollars, how would you **respond**? Write *yes*, *no*, or *maybe* beside each choice.

____ I'd put all the money in the bank.

____ I'd have a huge party.

____ I'd share it with my family.

2 **VERB ENDINGS**

A **verb ending** can be added to a verb to show when an action takes place. To show that an action happened in the past, you can often add *-ed*. To show that an action is happening in the present, you can often add *-ing*. If a verb ends with *e*, you usually drop the *e* before adding *-ed* or *-ing*.

Sometimes, I *exercise*.
Right now, I am *exercising*.
Yesterday, I *exercised*.

Add the verb. Use the correct verb ending.

1. Yesterday, she _____ to the email I sent. (**respond**)

2. Today, we _____ to get tickets to the concert. (want)

3. They are _____ us to the box office right now. (drive)

3 **Decide.** What part of your **identity** is most **unique**?

☐ your laugh
☐ your temper
☐ your handwriting
☐ your clothes

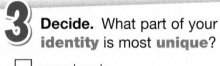

4 **Finish them.** Complete these sentences with **genuinely** or **error**.

In today's soccer game, my biggest _____ was scoring a point for the other team.
I was _____ embarrassed!

5 Check them. You may think someone is trying to **deceive** you if he or she says:

- ☐ "Let's do some yard work. Cutting grass will be lots of fun."
- ☐ "If you forward this email, you'll have good luck."
- ☐ "A bee is about to sting you!"
- ☐ "Just tell me. I promise I'll keep it a secret."

6 Choose one. Which word do you think has the closest meaning to **secure**?

- ☐ reliable
- ☐ risky
- ☐ respectable

7 Think about it. Some things need to be done **precisely**. Some things don't. Write *precisely* or *not precisely* next to each action.

brain surgery _____

watering the lawn _____

counting change _____

8 WORD FAMILIES

A **word family** is a group of words that share the same base word and have related meanings, such as *receive* and *receipt*. *Receive* means to be given something. A *receipt* is a piece of paper that shows that you have received something.

Which sentences use words that come from the same word family as identity?

- ☐ How will we identify the thief?
- ☐ I can't let you in without identification.
- ☐ My teeth fell out. I need dentures.

I hope you like it. But if you don't, I still have the **receipt**.

I'm so thankful to **receive** this gift!

9 Check them. Which of these people have voices you would **recognize** over the phone?

- ☐ your mother
- ☐ a local newspaper reporter
- ☐ your favorite movie star
- ☐ the President of the United States
- ☐ your first-grade teacher

10 Solve it. Use clues from the sentence below.

She yawned a lot and fell asleep in class.

It was really evident that:

- ☐ she was tired.
- ☐ she was lazy.

It was also evident that:

- ☐ she needed a laugh.
- ☐ she needed more sleep.

FINISH

Writing Text Type
Literary Analysis

A literary analysis carefully examines a text, or one element of a text, such as character, plot, setting, or theme in a story.

▶ Read student Mimi Ryan's analysis of character in "Louisa, Please Come Home."

Student Model

Topic Sentence

The **topic sentence** identifies the title, author, and text type that the writer will analyze.

1. **UNDERLINE** the topic sentence.

The topic sentence includes a **controlling idea** about the text or story element being analyzed.

2. **BOX** the controlling idea.

Detail Sentences

Detail sentences give supporting **evidence** from the text.

3. ✔ **CHECK** two pieces of supporting evidence.

Direct quotations from the text provide evidence for the analysis.

4. **DOUBLE UNDERLINE** two direct quotations.

Language Use

Transition words and phrases introduce and connect ideas.

5. **CIRCLE** three transitions.

Concluding Sentence

The **concluding sentence** sums up the writer's ideas about the text.

6. ★ **STAR** the concluding sentence.

The Selfish Sister
by Mimi Ryan

In the short story "Louisa, Please Come Home" by Shirley Jackson, the least likeable character is Louisa's sister, Carol. First of all, Carol makes Louisa feel insecure. Louisa worries about looking "like a ridiculous fool" around her older sister (65). Maybe this is one of the reasons she decides to leave home. Also, the way Carol reacts to Louisa's disappearance is extremely selfish. Instead of being concerned about her younger sister, Carol tells a reporter that Louisa "would never have wanted to spoil my wedding" (65). For these reasons, Carol is a selfish character who is a major cause of Louisa's problems.

Brainstorm

▶ Read the writing prompt. Then use the boxes to help you
   brainstorm your ideas.

Characters

Plot

Writing Prompt:
**Analyze character, plot,
setting, or theme in
"Louisa, Please Come Home."**

Setting

Theme

Choose Your Topic

▶ Select one of your ideas from the idea web. Then complete the sentences below.

I plan to analyze _____ in _____

In this story, _____

_____

Organize Ideas for Writing

▶ **Complete this outline with notes for your literary analysis paragraph.**

    I. Topic Sentence. State your main point about the text.

    Topic: _____

    Controlling Idea: _____

    II. Detail Sentences. List two pieces of evidence that support the topic sentence.

    Detail 1: _____

    Detail 2: _____

    III. Concluding Sentence. Restate your key ideas about the text.

    _____

    _____

Write Your Draft

▶ **Write a draft of your literary analysis.**

Writing Prompt:
Analyze character, plot, setting, or theme in "Louisa, Please Come Home."

WORD CHOICES	
Everyday	**Precise**
shows	indicates
says	states
nice	sympathetic

_____
(title of analysis)

▶ **Write your topic sentence.**

Topic Sentence

In the _____ by _____,
          (text type and title)   (author)

_____.
             (controlling idea)

▶ **Type your topic sentence on the computer or write it on paper. Then use these transition words and phrases to complete a draft of your paragraph.**

Detail Sentences

First of all, . . .	*For example, . . .*
In addition, . . .	*Furthermore, . . .*

Concluding Sentence

In conclusion, . . .	*To sum up, . . .*

Revise Your Paragraph

▶ **Evaluate:** Rate your analysis. Then have a writing partner rate it.

Scoring Guide

needs improvement	average	good	excellent
1	2	3	4

1. **UNDERLINE** the topic sentence. Does it identify the title, author, and text type?
   Self   1   2   3   4
   Partner   1   2   3   4

2. **BOX** the controlling idea. Does it tell what story element the writer will analyze?
   Self   1   2   3   4
   Partner   1   2   3   4

3. ✔**CHECK** the detail sentences. Do they give evidence from the text?
   Self   1   2   3   4
   Partner   1   2   3   4

4. **DOUBLE UNDERLINE** the direct quotations. Do they provide evidence for the analysis?
   Self   1   2   3   4
   Partner   1   2   3   4

5. **CIRCLE** the transition words and phrases. Do they introduce or connect ideas?
   Self   1   2   3   4
   Partner   1   2   3   4

6. ★**STAR** the concluding sentence. Does it sum up the writer's ideas about the text?
   Self   1   2   3   4
   Partner   1   2   3   4

▶ **Discuss:** Give feedback on your partner's literary analysis.

1. Start with positive comments about your partner's literary analysis.

You did an effective job of _____

_____

I appreciate the way you _____

_____

2. Give your partner suggestions for revision.

Your analysis should include _____

_____

Your detail sentences would be stronger if you _____

_____

Your concluding sentence needs _____

_____

_____

3. Answer any questions your partner has about your suggestions.

4. Ask your partner for feedback. Use the frames below to summarize your partner's feedback.

I did an effective job of . . .
You appreciated the way I . . .
You questioned why I . . .
My analysis needs . . .

▶ **Revise** Now revise your literary analysis.

Grammar CORRECTING RUN-ON SENTENCES

A **run-on sentence** is made up of two complete thoughts that are incorrectly joined together.

- To fix a run-on sentence, separate the ideas into two **complete sentences**.
- Or, insert a comma and a connecting word between the thoughts.

Example	
Run-on sentence:	Louisa lived here she ran away.
Complete sentences:	Louisa lived here. She ran away.
Complete sentence:	Louisa lived here, but she ran away.

▶ **Put an *R* next to the run-on sentences. Put a *C* next to the complete sentences.**

1. Louisa chose that day she wanted to ruin the wedding.   *R*

2. We miss our daughter she disappeared.   _____

3. No one stopped her Paul saw her leave.   _____

4. She got a good job when she reached Chandler.   _____

5. Mrs. Peacock was glad that Louisa saved some money.   _____

6. Louisa didn't miss her family she saw Paul again.   _____

▶ **Rewrite the run-on sentences below as complete sentences.**

7. Her mother didn't recognize her they had both changed.

_____

8. Even Louisa's father didn't know her he tried to be nice.

_____

9. He gave Louisa money she gave it to Paul.

_____

10. This story was depressing Louisa made some poor choices.

_____

▶ **Edit Your Draft.** Take a close look at the sentences in your draft. **Are any of them run-on sentences?** Fix the ones that are.

Usage USING CORRECT WORD ORDER

The **order of words** in a sentence must make sense.

- An adjective comes before the noun it describes.
- A helping verb comes just before the main verb in a statement.

Example	
Correct	**Incorrect**
Louisa bought a new coat.	Louisa bought a coat new.
I know where Louisa is going.	I know where is Louisa going.

▶ **Find and correct five errors in this paragraph.**

Student Model

> Louisa's family misunderstands her that is why she runs away from home. She feels no one really knows her, so she changes her idintity. Also, her sister probably said things cruel to her. Readers can tell that they don't get along very well. However, those problemes are not good reasons to leave home. Now, Louisa's family doesn't recognize her. I don't think Louisa knows what is she doing. She ends up losing the only family she has ever known.

CHECK AND CORRECT

- ☐ Correct one run-on sentence.
- ☐ **UNDERLINE** two word-order errors and correct them.
- ☐ (CIRCLE) two spelling errors and correct them.

▶ **Edit Your Draft.** Look at the sentences in your own draft. **Do they all use correct word order?** Fix the ones that do not.

Final Draft/Present

▶ **Write a final draft of your paragraph on the computer or on paper. Check it again and correct any errors before you present it.**

Analyze an Advertisement

Public service advertisements, or ads, try to share an important message or get people to use a service.

▶ **Read this billboard advertisement. Then answer the questions below.**

MARK IT

- **UNDERLINE** the headline of the advertisement.
- **CIRCLE** the ad's creators. This is called the signature.
- ★**STAR** the contact information for the creators.

READY TO GO HOME?

BROKE..HUNGRY... —AND— OUT OF LUCK!! KINDNESS HELPS PLEASE...

BETWEEN 1.6 AND 2.8 MILLION TEENS RUN AWAY FROM HOME EVERY YEAR.

But the streets can be a tough place. If you are a runaway between the ages of 12 and 20, and you need help returning home, call 1-800-Runaway or visit 1800runaway.org.

This is a public service ad by the Council for Runaway Youths.

❶ **How many teens run away each year?**

Ⓐ 16 million

Ⓑ more than 1.6 million

Ⓒ less than 1.6 million

Ⓓ more than 2.8 million

❷ **Who do you think this ad is designed for?**

Ⓐ parents of runaways

Ⓑ the general public

Ⓒ teens who want to run away from home

Ⓓ teens who have run away from home

❸ **What part of the ad do you think is the most effective? Why?**

The most effective part of the ad is

_____

_____

_____

_____

It is effective because _____

_____

_____

_____

Art Director
Maria Diaz

This art director designs ads, CD covers, movie posters, and more!

▶ **Read the weekly schedule and job information. Then answer the questions below about Maria Diaz's job.**

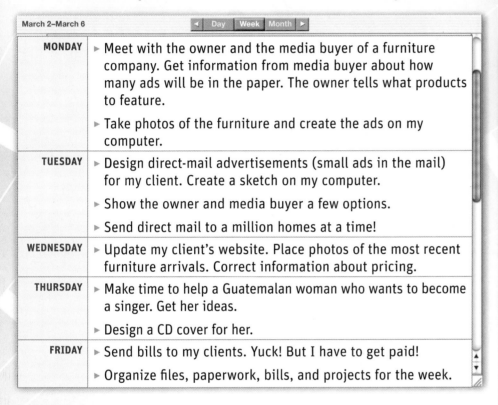

March 2–March 6	◄ Day **Week** Month ►
MONDAY	► Meet with the owner and the media buyer of a furniture company. Get information from media buyer about how many ads will be in the paper. The owner tells what products to feature. ► Take photos of the furniture and create the ads on my computer.
TUESDAY	► Design direct-mail advertisements (small ads in the mail) for my client. Create a sketch on my computer. ► Show the owner and media buyer a few options. ► Send direct mail to a million homes at a time!
WEDNESDAY	► Update my client's website. Place photos of the most recent furniture arrivals. Correct information about pricing.
THURSDAY	► Make time to help a Guatemalan woman who wants to become a singer. Get her ideas. ► Design a CD cover for her.
FRIDAY	► Send bills to my clients. Yuck! But I have to get paid! ► Organize files, paperwork, bills, and projects for the week.

1 **Maria Diaz works with a team to create media advertisements. How does she get feedback on her work?**

_____

_____

2 **How creative do you think Diaz's job is? Mark the line.**

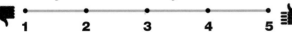

1   2   3   4   5

Not very creative   Very creative

3 **I would/would not (circle one) like Diaz's job because**

_____

_____

ON THE JOB

LOCATION

Simi Valley, California

EDUCATION

Bachelor's degree in Graphic Design

RESPONSIBILITIES

• Works with a variety of clients
• Creates designs
• Manages finances and paperwork for her company

SKILLS

• Following directions of clients
• Translating ideas into clear visual messages
• Using computer software to create art

SALARY

$50,000–$80,000

CAREER HIGHLIGHT

"I enjoy every day of my job. It doesn't feel like work!"

CAREER CONNECTION

Arts, A/V Technology, and Communication
www.careerclusters.org

Related Jobs
• website designer
• printing equipment operator
• computer animator

What should Louisa do?

You are a team of volunteers at a teen crisis center. Louisa has told you her problem. **Give Louisa advice** that will help her with the conflict.

❶ Identify the problem. Review the story "Louisa, Please Come Home." What is the problem at the end of the story?

From Louisa's point of view: _____

_____

_____

From her parents' point of view: _____

_____

❷ Evaluate evidence. Find three details from the story that show how much Louisa and her family want to be reunited.

Details About Louisa	Details About Louisa's Family
Louisa calls out to Paul when she sees him in the street.	

❸ Collaborate. Brainstorm three solutions that would benefit Louisa.

- *Louisa could apologize to her family and explain why she disappeared.*

- _____

  _____

- _____

  _____

- _____

④ **Prepare your role-play notes.** Review the story to make sure that you stay true to the characters.

ROLES:
- Crisis Counselor #1   - Crisis Counselor #2   - Louisa

Crisis Counselor #1: Louisa, please explain why you ran away.

Louisa: I ran away because _____

_____

_____

Crisis Counselor #2: Do you believe your family wants you to return home?

Louisa: Yes, because_____

_____

_____

Crisis Counselor #1: Louisa, what would make your family believe you are the real Louisa?

Louisa: My family has been deceived before. I would _____

_____

_____

Crisis Counselor #2: What would you say to make your family believe you want to return home?

Louisa: I would tell my family_____

_____

_____

_____

_____

Crisis Counselor #1: Louisa, thank you for coming to the crisis center. We think your problem can be solved, and we will help you return to your family.

Comprehension

▶ **Fill in the circle next to the correct answer.**

1. In "Louisa, Please Come Home," when does Louisa run away?
   Ⓐ on her birthday
   Ⓑ on New Year's Day
   Ⓒ on her sister's wedding day
   Ⓓ the day before her sister's wedding

> **Here's a Tip.**
> For short-answer questions, restate the question in your answer. This helps focus your response.

CRITICAL READING

2. **Evaluate:** What is Louisa's biggest problem?
   Ⓐ Her sister is competitive and mean.
   Ⓑ She is lazy and irresponsible.
   Ⓒ Her family refuses to recognize her.
   Ⓓ Her family becomes homeless.

3. How does Louisa's family react when they finally see her again?
   Ⓐ They cry with joy and excitement.
   Ⓑ They cry with disappointment and sadness.
   Ⓒ They tell her all about Carol's wedding.
   Ⓓ They tell her how much they've missed her.

4. What does Louisa do to resolve her problem as well as she can?
   Ⓐ She introduces Mrs. Peacock to her family.
   Ⓑ She tries to prove her real identity.
   Ⓒ She marries Paul.
   Ⓓ She returns to her new life with Mrs. Peacock.

CRITICAL READING

5. **Evaluate:** Which statement best states a theme of the poems on pages 74–75?
   Ⓐ It is useless to try to hide your real identity.
   Ⓑ It is risky, but important, to reveal your true identity to your family.
   Ⓒ People often get upset when you change something about yourself.
   Ⓓ Someone's private identity is not the same as the outward image that others see.

Vocabulary

▶ **Fill in the circle next to the correct definition of the underlined word.**

1. Louisa didn't look <u>unique</u>, so she blended in with the crowd.
   - (A) special and one-of-a-kind
   - (C) old-fashioned
   - (B) like all the others
   - (D) modern

2. Paul had no trouble <u>recognizing</u> Louisa.
   - (A) thinking she was someone else
   - (C) knowing who she was
   - (B) not understanding who she was
   - (D) all of the above

3. When Louisa's parents didn't believe Louisa, they were making an <u>error</u>.
   - (A) a story
   - (C) a mistake
   - (B) a discovery
   - (D) a problem

▶ **Choose the correct form of the underlined verb.**

4. Paul had <u>deceive</u> Louisa's family before.
   - (A) deceived
   - (C) deceiving
   - (B) deceives
   - (D) correct as is

▶ **Choose the correct word to complete the sentence.**

5. When Louisa moved to Chandler, she changed her _____.
   - (A) idea
   - (C) identity
   - (B) identify
   - (D) identical

Short Answer

▶ **Evaluate:** Use what you've read in this Workshop to answer the question below. Check your spelling and grammar.

CRITICAL READING

Would you want to be Louisa's friend? Why or why not?

_____

_____

_____

_____

_____

WORKSHOP 4

INFORMATIONAL TEXT

COMPREHENSION FOCUS
Summarize

CRITICAL READING FOCUS
Analyze

Synthesize

Reading 1 Life in the Dumps | **News Article**

Reading 2 Working in the Fields | **Magazine Article**

Reading 3 Child Labor Around the World | **Social Studies Text**

Stolen Childhoods

Around the world, 250 million children work for a living. From Mexico to Pakistan, they slave away on farms, in factories, and even in garbage dumps. These kids don't go to school. For most of them, school isn't even an option.

Why must kids work? What is being done to help them get back their childhoods?

Academic Vocabulary

◎ **Target Word**

▶ Read the Target Words. Rate each one using the scale below.*

Meaning

▶ Read the Target Word meanings. Write in the missing words.

Examples

▶ Finish the Target Word examples below. Write in the missing ones.

Target Word	Meaning	Examples
labor (p. 92) la•bor (noun) ① ② ③ ④	hard work	• One example of **labor** is _____ _____ • Someone who does tough **labor** _____
international (p. 92) in•ter•na•tion•al (adjective) ① ② ③ ④	relating to one or more _____	Child labor is an **international** problem that happens all over the world.
produce (p. 94) pro•duce (verb) ① ② ③ ④	to _____ something	• An electronics factory **produces** _____ • _____
benefit (p. 98) be•ne•fit (noun) ① ② ③ ④	a _____ result	• One **benefit** of playing a sport is _____ • When I pass my tests, I can see the **benefit** of _____ _____
economy (p. 100) e•con•o•my (noun) ① ② ③ ④	the way products and services are created, bought, and sold	• When the **economy** is strong, people _____ • _____

*Rating Scale
① = I don't know the word.   ③ = I think I know the word.
② = I've seen it or heard it.   ④ = I know it and use it.

The Key Idea

▶ **WRITE** What is this article mostly about?

_____

_____

VOCABULARY
Target Word

require

re•quire (verb)

Rate It: ① ② ③ ④

Meaning

_____ _something_

Example

My dad's job **requires** _him to_

_____

_____

React and Write

▶ **WRITE** Imagine that you could make laws and rules. What laws would you make to help child laborers like Tariah?

Summarize

In one or two sentences, summarize a typical workday for Tariah. Include the topic and important details.

News Article

Life in the Dumps

Children Sift Through Garbage

by Kris Saks

May 10, 2010—Every day, more than 1,000 children pick through mountains of garbage at the dump in Bekasi, Indonesia. Eleven-year-old Tariah is one of them.

Tariah does manual labor for a living. Every day, she picks through piles of rotting trash. Flies swarm around her head. Huge bulldozers roar nearby. Thick, dirty smoke stings her eyes.

Tariah hunts for tattered plastic bags. She also looks for scrap metal. Tariah's tiny hands bleed from touching broken glass. At the end of the day, she gives the trash to her boss. He resells it to recycling companies.

Tariah's job **requires** backbreaking work, but she earns only pennies a day. She gives the money to her parents. They need it for their family to survive.

Tariah wants to leave the dump. "I'm learning to read and write," she says. "I want to be a teacher."

A young girl in Indonesia works in a garbage dump.

Like Tariah, kids all over the world work in dumps. It's an international problem. These kids work for 9 to 12 hours a day. The lucky ones earn $16 a month. But they all lose much more. They miss out on school. They get sick. They don't have any fun. Worst of all, they have lost their childhoods. ⟨END⟩

Words to Know!	**manual**	by hand

Comprehension Focus

Summarize

A **summary** is a short statement of the most important ideas in a reading.
To summarize:

- Find the topic of the text.
- Look for the most important details about the topic.
- Restate the topic and important details in a short summary. Use your own words.

▶ **Complete this chart with the topic and important details in "Life in the Dumps."**

Topic

> _____
> _____
> _____
> _____

Details

1. _Eleven-year-old Tariah picks through piles of rotting trash._
   _____
2. _____
   _____
3. _____
   _____

Summarize

> ▶ **Now summarize the article.**
> **Check that you:**
> ❑ state the topic
> ❑ give important details about the topic
> ❑ use your own words

The Key Idea

▶ **WRITE** What is this article mostly about?

_____

_____

◎ Target Word

border

bor•der (noun)

Rate It: ① ② ③ ④

Meaning

the _____

that divides two countries

Example

If I crossed a **border**, I'd

probably see _____

_____

_____

① React and Write

▶ **WRITE** What do you do during your summer vacation? How does it compare to what James Flores does?

WORKING IN THE FIELDS

Across America, teens work in the fields, picking the crops that feed us.

by Lee Rosenberg

In the United States, nearly 150,000 teens are migrant workers. They travel from field to field, picking crops. These teens work in the sweltering heat. They sacrifice their time and freedom. They do it to help their families.

Summer Days

For seven years, James Flores has spent summers on a farm in Ohio. But James is not on vacation. He's working. The farm produces fruits and vegetables. James picks crops to help his family make ends meet. He works nine hours a day, six days a week. That's 54 hours—14 hours over the legal limit for kids.

In the U.S., teens work in the sweltering heat for little pay.

Sometimes James carries 50 pounds of cucumbers at a time. "The weight is heavy," says the 14-year-old.

"It's hard to take. But the hardest part is not having fun. I'd rather be playing than working."

Crossing the Border

Many teens come from other countries to find work in the U.S. Why? They want to help their families back home. In their home countries, families earn barely enough to get by.

Many of these workers come here legally. But some cross our **borders** illegally. Seventeen-year-old Rodrigo Perez comes here illegally. He is from Guatemala. He works on a farm in Massachusetts. To get to his job, Rodrigo has to travel over 2,200 miles.

Rodrigo works hard at his job, but he earns little more than the minimum wage. He doesn't even keep the money for himself. He sends most of his pay home to Guatemala. "I send money to help my family live better," he says.

Rodrigo isn't alone. Between 60 and 80 percent of migrant workers are from other countries. Together, these workers send millions of dollars home to Latin America and the Caribbean. ➤

| Words to Know! | **sacrifice** to give up |

Summarize

1. ▶ **WRITE** What is the topic of "Summer Days"?

_____

_____

2. **UNDERLINE** Identify two details in "Summer Days" that tell more about the topic.

3. Summarize the section in your own words to a partner.

4. ▶ **WRITE** What is the topic of "Crossing the Border"?

_____

_____

5. (CIRCLE) Identify two details in "Crossing the Border" that tell more about the topic.

6. Summarize the section in your own words to a partner.

CRITICAL READING
Synthesize

▶ **WRITE** Imagine working nine hours a day, six days a week. What effects would this work schedule have on your education and your social life?

_____

_____

_____

_____

_____

Active Reading

UNDERLINE Why does Jessica give her father half of her wages?

VOCABULARY
Target Word

resources

re•sour•ces *(noun)*

Rate It: ① ② ③ ④

Meaning

supplies that you _____ to _____ something

Example

Water and air are natural resources we need to _____

React and Write

▶ **WRITE** Do you think that kids in the U.S. should do farm labor? Why or why not?

Summarize

In one or two sentences, summarize the topic and important details in "Families Working Together."

"I feel proud to make money to help support my family," James says.

Families Working Together

Many U.S. teens do farm labor alongside their families. Half of these families earn less than $10,000 a year. Mothers, fathers, and children must all work to pay the bills.

Fourteen-year-old Jessica Roman works with her father and brothers. She picks blueberries all day long. It is exhausting work. But she gives half of her wages to her father. The money helps pay the family's bills.

James Flores works with his parents, two sisters, and eight brothers. "I feel proud to make money to help support my family," James says.

"Many migrant children help feed and clothe the family," says Jeanne Cure. She works for a group that helps migrant families. Workers get paid by the amount they pick, Cure explains. "If their kids help, it means more hands picking."

A Better Life

What can be done to help young field workers? The Migrant Education Program offers many **resources**, such as free tutoring and health services.

A girl picks grapes in a California field.

Rodrigo is one of 620,000 young people in the program. He goes to classes four nights a week.

"I go because I want to learn English," he says. "I want a better life." *END*

Words to Know! **exhausting** very tiring

Comprehension Focus

Summarize

▶ **Complete this chart with the topic and important details in "Working in the Fields."**

Topic

_____

_____

_____

Details

1. _____

_____

_____

2. _____

_____

_____

3. _____

_____

_____

Summarize

▶ **Now summarize the article. Check that you:**

❑ state the topic

❑ give important details about the topic

❑ use your own words

💡 The Key Idea

▶ **WRITE** What is this social studies text mostly about?

_____

_____

◎ VOCABULARY
Target Word

deprive

de•prive (verb)

Rate It: ① ② ③ ④

Meaning

to _____

someone something they

_____

Example

*If you **deprive** a plant of water, it will* _____

_____

❗ React and Write

▶ **WRITE** Would you use a soccer ball that a young child laborer made? Why or why not?

CHILD LABOR
Around the World

On dusty farms and in hot factories, kids slave away. They earn only pennies a day.

by Nelda Marquez

A Global Problem

Around the world, over 250 million children and teens work for a living. They spend their days on farms and in factories. Some work full-time. Others work part-time. But they all work for very little pay. These children are **deprived** of a normal childhood. They can't even go to school. The only benefit of their jobs is the little money they give to their parents.

Child labor is a global problem. In Brazil, close to 150,000 children pick oranges. They work in extreme heat for up to 12 hours a day. Their fingertips are blistered from pesticides. In Pakistan, close to 12 million children stitch together soccer balls and sportswear. Some are as young as five years old. And in Indonesia, teens suffer in hot, stuffy factories. They lace up $100 tennis shoes for only 15 cents an hour.

Words to Know!	**pesticides** chemicals used to kill insects that destroy crops

This child's job is to stitch together soccer balls.

Real Kids, Real Lives

These kids aren't just statistics. They have faces and names—just like you.

Bonauli works seven days a week on a fishing pier in Indonesia. He rarely sees his family. "I miss my mom," he says. But his mother lives very far away.

In Istanbul, Turkey, 11-year-old Muhsin sells travel packages of tissues on a street corner. His customers are taxi drivers. Muhsin goes from car to car when they stop at traffic lights. On a good day, Muhsin sells enough to buy a handful of crackers for lunch.

Eleven-year-old Muhammad works on a tea farm in India. From 5 A.M. until 9:30 P.M. he picks tea leaves. "My boss beats me," he says. "It is my dream, for just one day, to go to school."

Thousands of kids around the world feel like Muhammad. But their dreams may never come true. ➤

 **Summarize**

1. ▶ **WRITE** What is the topic of "A Global Problem"?

_____

_____

2. <u>UNDERLINE</u> Mark two important details in "A Global Problem."

3. Summarize the section in your own words to a partner.

4. ▶ **WRITE** What is the topic of "Real Kids, Real Lives"?

_____

_____

5. ✔ **CHECK** Identify two important details in "Real Kids, Real Lives."

6. Summarize the section in your own words to a partner.

REVIEW
Sequence

(CIRCLE) In "Real Kids, Real Lives," when does Muhammad work?

CRITICAL READING
Analyze

▶ **WRITE** How could education help to stop child labor?

_____

_____

_____

_____

_____

Active Reading

★**STAR** What happened when school fees were banned in Kenya?

VOCABULARY
Target Word

reform

re•form (verb)

Rate It: ① ② ③ ④

Meaning

to make something _____

_____ by

_____

Example

Prisons help **reform** people who commit crime by _____

_____

React and Write

▶**WRITE** Do you think education should be free for all children everywhere? Why or why not?

Summarize

▶**WRITE** Summarize the topic and important details in the social studies text "Child Labor Around the World."

From Work to School

There are many complicated reasons why children must work. In Kenya, the problem began in 1982. During that year, the country was faced with major debts. To pay them, the government decided to charge a fee to attend school. Families had to pay up to $350 per year. This was a huge amount of money in Kenya's economy. On average, Kenyans make only $1 a day. School became a luxury. Few could afford it.

Most parents couldn't pay the school fee. Instead, they sent their kids to work. Many children were sent to pick coffee beans in dangerous conditions. In 2002, 4 million Kenyan kids worked instead of going to school.

Finally, in 2003, the Kenyan government banned the school fees. Overnight, school enrollment boomed. One and a half million kids showed up to learn.

Words to Know! **luxury** something very rich and special

TEXT FEATURE Reading a Time Line

Key Events in Child Labor History

Because of World War II, child labor laws are relaxed to allow teenagers to work in wartime factories.
1943

Iqbal Masih, a former child slave turned child labor activist, is murdered.
1995

The United Nations Convention on the Rights of the Child turns 20 years old. Its terms are now accepted by 194 nations around the world.
2009

1938
The Fair Labor Standards Act—establishing child labor standards in the U.S.—is signed into law.

1989
The United Nations unanimously adopts the Convention on the Rights of the Child, which spells out the basic human rights of children around the world.

2004
The Children's World Congress holds the first ever global youth congress on child labor in Florence, Italy. Five hundred kids, aged 10 to 17, gather to share their perspectives on child labor.

Kids in Kenya can now go to school for free.

Ending Child Labor

Experts around the world agree. Education is the key to ending child labor. But even in Kenya, only elementary school is free. High school costs money. In many other nations, there is no free public education.

Many people are working together to **reform** child labor. The United Nations assists children who work by giving them food and medicine. In the U.S., many citizens protest products made by child labor. Their goal is clear—to end child labor for good.

A time line shows key events in history.

❶ When was the Fair Labor Standards Act signed into law?

Ⓐ 1938   Ⓑ 1943   Ⓒ 1995   Ⓓ 2004

❷ What happened to U.S. child labor laws in 1943?

Ⓐ They were approved by the U.N.

Ⓑ They were protested by a group of 500 kids.

Ⓒ They were relaxed to allow teens to work in factories.

Ⓓ Ten-year-olds were allowed to work in schools.

❸ **Synthesize:** Would Iqbal Masih have been pleased by the time line entry for 2009? Why or why not?

_____

_____

_____

Summarize

1. ▶ **WRITE** What is the topic of "From Work to School"?

_____

_____

2. (CIRCLE) Find two important details in "From Work to School."

3. Summarize the section in your own words to a partner.

CRITICAL READING
Synthesize

✔ **CHECK** What message do you get from both the time line and pages 100–101 of the reading?

❏ Child labor is here to stay.
❏ Child labor is more common now than it was 20 years ago.
❏ Many people are working to end child labor.

Skills Check

1. ▶ **WRITE** What is the topic of "Ending Child Labor"?

_____

_____

2. **UNDERLINE** Find two important details in "Ending Child Labor."

3. Write a summary of this section on the computer or on paper.

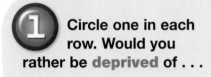

Word Challenge

Start

1 **Circle one in each row.** Would you rather be **deprived** of . . .

- television **OR** video games?

- friends **OR** family?

- radio **OR** music videos?

- sleep **OR** food?

2 ## Using a Dictionary

Guide Words are the words on the top of the dictionary pages. They tell the first and last words listed on those pages.

Write each Target Word next to the words that could be its guide words.

international	labor	produce

Guide Words	**Target Words**
problematic ➤ profitability	_____
internal ➤ intro	_____
know ➤ ladder	_____

produce ➤ prohibit

pro·duce
1. (pruh-**dooss**) *verb* To make something. *This factory produces cars.*
2. (**prod**-ooss or **proh**-dooss) *noun* Things that are produced or grown for eating, especially fruits and . . .

3 **List them.** You just won an **international** trip to three countries. Which countries would you visit?

1. _____
2. _____
3. _____

Which three **international** cities would you visit?

1. _____
2. _____
3. _____

4 **Check it.** Which of these would you most like to **produce** someday?

☐ cool music   ☐ other: _____

☐ great art   _____

☐ an action movie   _____

5 **You choose.** Your school just got money for a new **resource**. Which do you vote for?

☐ a gym with a pool and weight room

☐ a student lounge with comfortable couches

☐ a health center with a full-time nurse and doctor

☐ a recording studio for musicians and singers

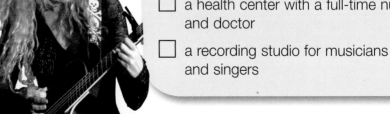

6
Rate them. Which of these tasks would **require** the most **labor** for you? Rate them from 1 to 4.

1 = **requires** the most **labor**
4 = **requires** the least **labor**

____ drawing a self-portrait

____ cooking a dinner for four

____ baby-sitting eight kids

____ cleaning up your school

8 Multiple-Meaning Words

Multiple-meaning words are words that have more than one meaning.

Read the definitions for each multiple-meaning word. Use them to complete the sentences below.

benefit: 1. *(noun)* a good result
2. *(noun)* a performance to raise money for a charity

bowl: 1. *(noun)* a round container
2. *(verb)* to roll a heavy ball toward game pins

track: 1. *(noun)* a narrow road or path
2. *(verb)* to search

- Detectives followed the train _____, hoping to _____ down the thief.

- One _____ of having a _____ is raising money for a good cause.

- Tyra loves to _____, especially if she can snack on a _____ of popcorn at the same time.

7
Think about it. List some **benefits** of being famous.

_____
_____
_____

What would ***not*** be a **benefit** of being famous?

_____
_____
_____

9
Evaluate. Read each statement. Write ***A*** for agree or ***D*** for disagree. Be ready to defend your point of view.

____ Laws against street skateboarding should be **reformed**.

____ School rules about dress codes should be **reformed**.

____ Laws that say drivers must be 16 or older must be **reformed**.

10
Finish them. Complete these sentences with **border** or **economy**.

I contribute to the
_____
by buying clothes regularly.

My annoying little brother and I share a room. We drew a
_____
down the middle, separating his half from mine.

Finish

Writing Text Type
Informational Summary

An **informational summary** provides an overview of the key topics and ideas from a text.

▶ **Read student Ray Vasquez's summary of "Working in the Fields."**

Introduction

An **introductory statement** identifies the title, author, and text type that the writer will summarize.

1. **UNDERLINE** the introductory statement.

A **focus statement** states the plan for the paper.

2. **BOX** the focus statement.

Body

Body paragraphs cite **key topics and details** from the summarized text. Each body paragraph starts with a **topic sentence** that includes a controlling idea.

3. **UNDERLINE** the topic sentence in each paragraph.

4. ✔ **CHECK** three **key topics and details** cited from the text.

Language Use

Transition words and phrases connect ideas in the summary.

5. **CIRCLE** four transitions.

Citations from the text appear in quotation marks, with page numbers in parentheses.

6. **DOUBLE UNDERLINE** two citations.

Conclusion

The **conclusion** restates the focus statement and adds a final thought.

7. ★ **STAR** the conclusion.

Student Model

The Harsh Lives of Teen Migrant Workers
by Ray Vasquez

The magazine article "Working in the Fields," by Lee Rosenberg, describes the difficult lives of teen migrant workers. Rosenberg discusses the hard labor that teen migrant workers perform and the sacrifices they make to earn money for their families.

Rosenberg begins by discussing the tiring jobs teen migrant workers have. They work long hours in the fields, picking fruits and vegetables. For instance, one teen "works nine hours a day, six days a week" (94). The teen workers labor in the hot sun, and carry heavy loads of crops.

Another point the author makes is that teen migrant workers make major sacrifices to help their families have better lives. They give up their free time and summers to work. Often, they travel to the U.S. from other countries. One worker must "travel over 2,200 miles" (95). Some teens take great risks and come here illegally. Then, they send most of their income back home to help their poor families.

To sum up, Rosenberg illustrates the harsh lives of teen migrant workers. His article also mentions resources that help teens get out of the fields and into the classroom.

Analyze the Text Type

▶ **Work with a partner to understand the purpose and form of an informational summary.**

Purpose: Informational Summary

The purpose of an informational summary is _____

_____

Introduction

The **introductory paragraph** of an informational summary includes:

1. an _____
   that identifies the text, author, and text type to be summarized.
2. a focus statement that states the _____ for the paper.

Student Model | In his introduction, Vasquez:

1. identifies the title, author, and text type of the text he will summarize, which are:
   _____

2. gives a plan for discussing the topic, which is _____
   _____

Body

The **body paragraphs** cite key topics and details from the summarized text.

1. Each paragraph starts with a _____
2. The rest of the sentences give details that support the _____

Student Model

1. The topic sentence of the first body paragraph is: _____
   _____

2. List two key topics and details Vasquez includes in his first body paragraph.

   • _____
   • _____

Conclusion

The **conclusion** _____ the _____ statement.

Student Model | Vasquez concludes by restating _____
_____ and then adding _____

Brainstorm

▶ Read the writing prompt in the middle of the idea web. Then use the boxes to identify ideas and details from the text you will summarize.

Important Idea

Details to Support This Idea

Writing Prompt:
Write an informational summary of "Child Labor Around the World."

Important Idea

Details to Support This Idea

State Your Topic

▶ Use your ideas from the idea web to help you determine your topic.

I plan to summarize the Social Studies text _____

which discusses the topic of _____

_____

Organize Ideas for Writing

▶ Complete this outline with notes for your informational summary.

I. Introduction List details about the text you will summarize.

    A. Text Type: _____

    B. Title: _____

    C. Author: _____

    D. Topic: _____

    E. My Focus Statement: _____

    _____

II. Body Write a topic sentence for each body paragraph that includes a controlling idea. Then list two key details that support the topic sentence.

    A. Topic Sentence 1: _____

    _____

        Detail 1: _____

        Detail 2: _____

    B. Topic Sentence 2: _____

    _____

        Detail 1: _____

        Detail 2: _____

III. Conclusion In two sentences, restate the focus statement and add an interesting final thought.

    _____

    _____

    _____

    _____

Write Your Draft

▶ **Write a draft of your informational summary.**

Writing Prompt:
Write an informational summary of "Child Labor Around the World."

WORD CHOICES	
Everyday	**Precise**
work	labor
change	transform
yearly	annual
big problem	serious issue

_____
(summary title)

Introduction

▶ **Write your introductory statement.**

The _____
(text type, title, and author)

discusses _____
(topic)

▶ **Write your focus statement or plan.**

The _____ describes
(text type)

_____

and _____

_____

▶ **Type your introductory paragraph on the computer or write it on paper. Then use these transition words and phrases to help you complete a draft of your informational summary.**

Body

The text begins . . .	For instance, . . .
The text points out . . .	The most important point . . .
In addition, . . .	It also notes that . . .

Conclusion

Overall, . . .	To sum up, . . .
In conclusion, . . .	This article explains . . .

Revise Your Summary

► **Evaluate: Rate your summary. Then have a writing partner rate it.**

	Scoring Guide		
needs improvement	average	good	excellent
1	2	3	4

1. **<u>UNDERLINE</u>** the introductory statement. Does it state the title, author, and text type?
   Self   1   2   3   4
   Partner   1   2   3   4

2. **BOX** the focus statement. Does it state the plan for the paper?
   Self   1   2   3   4
   Partner   1   2   3   4

3. **<u>UNDERLINE</u>** the topic sentences in the body paragraphs. Do they include the controlling idea?
   Self   1   2   3   4
   Partner   1   2   3   4

4. ✔**CHECK** details in each body paragraph. Do they give information about the text?
   Self   1   2   3   4
   Partner   1   2   3   4

5. **CIRCLE** transition words and phrases. Do they connect ideas?
   Self   1   2   3   4
   Partner   1   2   3   4

6. **<u>DOUBLE UNDERLINE</u>** the citations. Do they appear in quotation marks with page numbers in parentheses?
   Self   1   2   3   4
   Partner   1   2   3   4

7. ★**STAR** the concluding sentence. Does it restate the focus statement?
   Self   1   2   3   4
   Partner   1   2   3   4

► **Discuss: Give feedback on your partner's informational summary.**

1. Start with positive comments about your partner's informational summary.

   You did an effective job of _____

   _____

   I appreciate the way you _____

   _____

2. Give your partner suggestions for revision.

   I have a question about _____

   _____

   The focus statement would be clearer if

   you _____

   _____

   Your summary needs _____

   _____

3. Answer any questions your partner has about your suggestions.

4. Ask your partner for feedback. Use the frames below to summarize your partner's feedback.

   The strongest part of my summary is . . .
   You appreciated the way I . . .
   You had a question about . . .
   My summary needs . . .

► **Revise** Now revise your informational summary.

Grammar USING CORRECT VERB TENSE

The **tense** of a verb shows when the action happened.

• A **present-tense verb** shows action that is happening now.

• A **past-tense verb** shows action that took place in the past.
  Most past-tense verbs end in *-ed*.

Example

Present-Tense Verb	Past-Tense Verb
James **works** on a farm.	James **worked** on a farm last summer.
James **picks** fruit.	James **picked** fruit yesterday.

▶ **Identify the tense of the verb in each sentence below by writing present or past on the line to the right.**

1. Tariah worked in the garbage dump. _____*past*_____

2. Migrant farmers produce food for many people. _____

3. The families worked in the sun all day. _____

4. James carried piles of cucumbers every day. _____

5. Muhsin sells tissues to cabdrivers. _____

6. He misses his grandparents very much. _____

▶ **Rewrite the sentences below using the past tense form of the verb.**

7. Rodrigo travels from Guatemala to the U.S.

_____

8. He works on a farm in the U.S.

_____

9. The migrant workers earn little money.

_____

10. Tutors help young farm workers.

_____

▶ **Edit Your Draft.** Take a close look at each sentence in your draft. **Does each sentence use correct verb tense?** Fix the ones that do not.

Mechanics USING COMMAS IN A SERIES

Items in a series are separated by **commas**.

- A series is a list of the same kinds of words.
- Commas follow every item in a series except the last one.

Example

Correct	Incorrect
Snakebites, cuts, and other injuries are part of the job.	Snakebites cuts and other injuries are part of the job.

▶ **Find and correct five errors in this paragraph.**

Student Model

> The article "Life in the Dumps" describes the problem of child laber in dumps. First, it tells Tariah's story. She shifts through trash looking for scrap metal glass and plastic bags. Then, it explains how she must sell the garbage. This supported her family. Finally, it explains how child labor is an internashonal problem.

CHECK AND CORRECT

- ☐ Insert two missing commas.
- ☐ Correct one verb-tense error.
- ☐ **CIRCLE** two spelling errors and correct them.

▶ **Edit Your Draft.** Look at the sentences in your own draft. **Do they use commas in a series correctly?** Fix the ones that do not.

Final Draft/Present

▶ **Write a final draft of your summary on the computer or on paper. Check it again and correct any errors before you present it.**

Focus Skill | Evaluate Sources

Use a Website

A website can help you find information. However, you must check a website carefully to make sure you can trust the information.

▶ **Read this website home page. Then answer the questions below about evaluating a website's information.**

> **MARK IT**
>
> - **UNDERLINE** the web address of this page.
> - **CIRCLE** where you go to contact the site owners.
> - ★**STAR** the date the site was last updated.

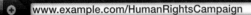

www.example.com/HumanRightsCampaign

Arianne's
HUMAN RIGHTS CAMPAIGN

HOME

ABOUT US

CONTACT US

CAUSES

DONATE

CLICK here to find out what you can do to protect human rights!

Are you concerned about the rights of people around the world? So are we! We research human rights in places as far away as Liberia and China.

Our goal is to help children and adults who are abused. We have many success stories, including helping to win freedom for child laborers in a Pakistan rug factory. Visit our Causes page to find out more about our accomplishments.

Want to get involved? Donate now! Your money will benefit a child or adult worker who needs it!

 CLICK for Arianne's latest report on human rights news from around the world.

Website last updated: August 2010.

Arianne and senior staff member Lei Ling (her sister) edit their newest report on human rights.

❶ **To learn more about who runs this site, what link would you click?**

Ⓐ Contact Us

Ⓑ About Us

Ⓒ Causes

Ⓓ Donate

❷ **What details on this website would require you to double-check the information it gives?**

Ⓐ The site is run by an individual, not an expert or official organization.

Ⓑ The site was last updated more than 10 years ago.

Ⓒ The site has many misspelled words.

Ⓓ all of the above

❸ **What could you do or where could you go to double-check the information on this site?**

_____

_____

_____

_____

_____

_____

_____

Human Rights Advocate
Ahmed Sirleaf

This advocate works to bring peace and justice to his home country.

▶ **Read the work schedule and job information. Then answer the questions below about Ahmed Sirleaf's job.**

October 14–October 18	◀ Day **Week** Month ▶
MONDAY	▶ Conference opening. Today is the first day of a conference that helps people deal with problems caused by war and poverty in Liberia. There are over 500 participants and many speakers here. Some of them are young people forced to work as child soldiers during the war.
TUESDAY	▶ Briefings. We hear from groups that interview victims of violence, and those who were violent to others.
WEDNESDAY	▶ Recording data. I lead a small group meeting on amnesty. Amnesty is when people are forgiven for their crimes. For example, child soldiers might not be fully responsible for the crimes they commit. I listen to people in the meeting who are experts or victims. I make sure I understand each person's point of view and record it accurately.
THURSDAY	▶ Long day! I work until midnight helping to write a summary of the conference findings.
FRIDAY	▶ Closing time. We present our summary to the conference participants. Conference leaders discuss and plan how to continue working for the people who need our help.

① The participants in Ahmed Sirleaf's meetings are different sources of information. How does he evaluate what they say?

_____

_____

_____

② How important is Sirleaf's job? Mark the line.

1 — 2 — 3 — 4 — 5

Not very important   Very important

③ I think Sirleaf's job is/isn't (circle one) important because

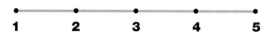

_____

_____

ON THE JOB

EDUCATION

Bachelor's degree in legal studies; Master's degree in international law

RESPONSIBILITIES

• Gathers information
• Works with a team
• Summarizes and presents information

SKILLS

• Interviewing people
• Researching and conducting investigations
• Recording and analyzing data

SALARY

$25,000–$60,000

WHY MY WORK MATTERS

"Growing up in Liberia, I saw brutal violence during the war. As a teenager, I couldn't do much. Now, I can help the country move forward."

CAREER CONNECTION

Law, Public Safety, Corrections, and Security
www.careerclusters.org

Related Jobs
• human rights lawyer
• legal youth advocate
• court reporter

What are your rights?

What are five basic rights that all young people should have? Create a bill of rights for young people, for the website of an international organization that fights child labor.

1 Take notes. Review the readings in this Workshop. For each reading, list two facts or details about how child workers are treated unfairly.

Reading 1: "Life in the Dumps"

- *children exposed to garbage that can damage health*

- _____

Reading 2: "Working in the Fields"

- _____

- _____

Reading 3: "Child Labor Around the World"

- _____

- _____

2 Collaborate. What are the most important rights based on your notes above? Complete this bill of rights that all young people should have.

Basic Rights for Young People Around the World
Young people should have the right to:
• a clean and safe environment.

❸ **Organize your home page.** Write five statements of rights below. Include other information that a website needs.

WEBSITE NAME:

Home Page	About Us	News	Contact Us	Multimedia

Statement of Purpose

Our organization's purpose is to

Five Rights for Young People

1. *All young people should have the right to a clean and safe environment.*

2. *All young people should*

3. *All young people should*

4. *All young people should*

5. *All young people should*

Site last updated: _____ Site created by: _____

Comprehension

▶ **Fill in the circle next to the correct answer.**

1. Why are there so many child laborers around the world?

Ⓐ Their families own the businesses where they work.

Ⓑ They prefer working to attending school.

Ⓒ They are born to poor families and must work to survive.

Ⓓ There are no schools close enough for them to attend.

CRITICAL READING

2. Analyze: Many teen migrant workers work long hours in the fields. What is a likely <u>effect</u> of this heavy workload for teens?

Ⓐ Most migrant workers work shorter hours in winter.

Ⓑ The teen workers leave to run their own farms.

Ⓒ Most migrant workers come from other nations.

Ⓓ The work interferes with the teen workers' education.

CRITICAL READING

3. Synthesize: What do you think is the overall message of "Child Labor Around the World"?

Ⓐ Child labor isn't a widespread problem.

Ⓑ Child labor happens only in America.

Ⓒ Child labor is an international problem that needs a solution.

Ⓓ Child labor is bad, but there's nothing we can do.

4. Why did the Kenyan government start charging money for children to go to school?

Ⓐ They thought kids would work harder.

Ⓑ Because the economy was bad, the Kenyan government needed the money.

Ⓒ Coffee farmers wanted more younger workers.

Ⓓ Schools became very expensive because they had computers.

5. What happened when the Kenyan government made schools free again?

Ⓐ Many children stopped working and enrolled in schools.

Ⓑ All students dropped out.

Ⓒ Coffee planters protested.

Ⓓ Students couldn't afford the bus fare to school.

Vocabulary

▶ **Fill in the circle next to the correct definition of the underlined word.**

1. The economy of Kenya is dependent on coffee.
   - Ⓐ the way people enjoy their life
   - Ⓑ the way money is made and shared
   - Ⓒ the size of the country
   - Ⓓ the rainfall

2. Around the world, child labor is a big problem.
   - Ⓐ rest
   - Ⓑ dining
   - Ⓒ recess
   - Ⓓ hard work

3. Often, international attention can help stop the abuse of child workers.
   - Ⓐ American
   - Ⓑ from more than one country
   - Ⓒ television
   - Ⓓ student

▶ **Choose the correct definition for the underlined multiple-meaning word.**

4. The car factory will no longer produce last year's popular model.
   - Ⓐ eat
   - Ⓑ suffer from
   - Ⓒ vegetables
   - Ⓓ make

▶ **Which are the most likely dictionary guide words for the underlined word?**

5. One benefit of an education is preparation for a good job.
   - Ⓐ *bat* and *batch*
   - Ⓑ *better* and *butter*
   - Ⓒ *belt* and *bet*
   - Ⓓ *drawback* and *bonus*

Short Answer

CRITICAL READING

▶ **Synthesize:** Use what you've read in this Workshop to answer the question below. Check your spelling and grammar.

What do you think is the worst thing about child labor? Why?

_____

_____

_____

_____

WORKSHOP 5

INFORMATIONAL TEXT

COMPREHENSION FOCUS
Problem and Solution

CRITICAL READING FOCUS
Analyze

Evaluate

Reading 1 Tragic Death on Train | **News Article**

Reading 2 The Secrets of Self-Esteem |
Magazine Article

Reading 3 The Power of Peer Pressure |
Life Skills Feature

UNDER PRESSURE

Being a teenager is tough. Teens are under serious pressure from their peers. It's not always easy to handle.

Sometimes teens pressure each other into making bad decisions. They do dangerous stunts. They make fun of the unpopular kids. Sometimes they really hurt each other.

You have to make the choice. It's not an easy one. Can you take the pressure?

Academic Vocabulary

Target Word	Meaning	Example
◎ ▶ Read the Target Words. Rate each one using the scale below.*	▶ Read the Target Word meanings. Write in the missing words.	▶ Finish the Target Word examples below. Write in the missing ones.
pressure (p. 120) pres•sure (noun) ① ② ③ ④	a force or a stressful _____ _____	• At _____, I am under **pressure** to _____ _____ • _____ _____
negative (p. 120) neg•a•tive (adjective) ① ② ③ ④	bad, harmful	• A **negative** thing some teens do is _____ _____ • _____ _____
authority (p. 123) au•thor•i•ty (noun) ① ② ③ ④	someone who _____ _____ about something	I am a top **authority** on fashion.
confidence (p. 123) con•fi•dence (noun) ① ② ③ ④	_____ _____ to do things well	• I have **confidence** that _____ • _____ _____
convince (p. 124) con•vince (verb) ① ② ③ ④	to make someone believe or do something	• _____ is always trying to **convince** me to _____ _____ • _____

*Rating Scale
① = I don't know the word.   ③ = I think I know the word.
② = I've seen it or heard it.   ④ = I know it and use it.

The Key Idea

▶ **WRITE** What is this article mostly about?

_____

_____

Target Word

rebel

re•bel (verb)

Rate It: ① ② ③ ④

Meaning

to _____ against

someone in a position of

_____

Example

Teens might **rebel** against

their parents by _____

_____

React and Write

▶ **WRITE** Describe a time when you faced negative peer pressure. Did you stand up for what you knew was right? Why or why not?

Summarize

In one or two sentences summarize how peer pressure cost Eric his life. Include the topic and important details.

Tragic Death on Train

Peer Pressure Costs Teen His Life

October 26—For Eric Alvarez, keeping up a cool image was more important than anything—even his safety. Peer pressure was a problem that cost him his life.

Eric rode the subway home from school every day. For fun, his friends would pry open the doors of the speeding cars. They would lean out into the tunnels. Eric went along.

Eric's aunt knew what he was doing and warned him to stop. "It's better to be called a chicken," she said. Eric **rebelled**—and did something even worse.

Last Monday, Eric really wanted to impress his friends. He decided to "surf" the subway. Eric's girlfriend tried to stop him. "Don't do it!" she begged, but Eric didn't listen.

Eric climbed to the roof of a speeding subway car. His head hit a beam. He fell—dead—onto the tracks.

Eric Alvarez poses for a school photo.

Eric's uncle is sure that peer pressure was to blame. "His friends pressured him to do it," he said.

These same friends attended Eric's funeral. Many had also "surfed" trains. A speaker at the funeral offered a solution. He said that teens must be brave enough to fight against negative peer pressure—because peer pressure can kill. END

Words to Know! **impress** to make someone admire something

Comprehension Focus
Problem and Solution

A **problem** is a situation or event that causes trouble. A **solution** is what fixes the problem. To find the problem and the solution:

- Look for signal words or phrases such as *problem, difficulty, conflict, challenge*.
- Look for attempts or ways to solve the problem.
- Look for signal words or phrases such as *solution, answer,* and *results were*.

▶ **Complete this chart with the problem and solution in "Tragic Death on Train."**

Problem

Peer pressure led Eric to perform dangerous subway stunts with his friends.

Attempt 1

Attempt 2

Solution

The Key Idea

▶ **WRITE** What is this article mostly about?

_____

_____

VOCABULARY
Target Word

constant

con•stant (adjective)

Rate It: ① ② ③ ④

Meaning

all the _____

Example

_____

_____ is constant

in my life these days.

React and Write

▶ **WRITE** What qualities do you most value in others? Good looks or what's on the inside? Be honest!

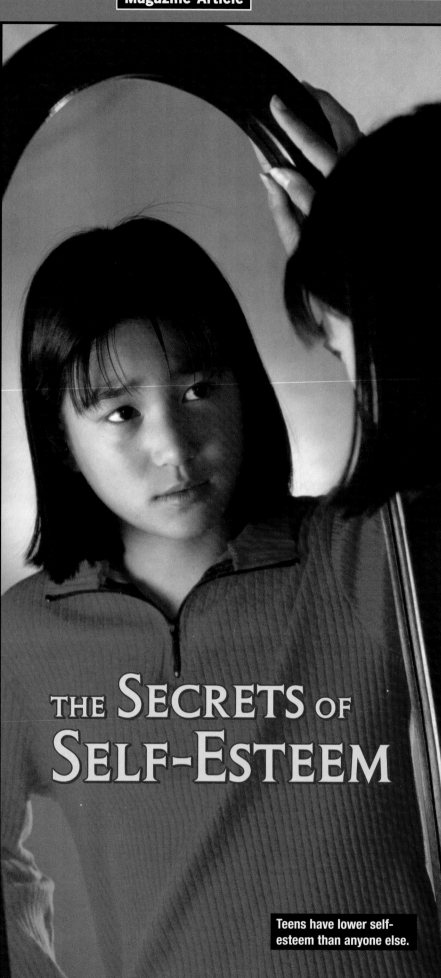

THE SECRETS OF SELF-ESTEEM

Teens have lower self-esteem than anyone else.

Many teens don't respect themselves. It's a big problem. What's the solution?

Many teens are in big trouble. Every day, they deal with a **constant** problem. The problem is pressure that comes from inside themselves. It's called low self-esteem.

Teen Self-Esteem

"Self-esteem" means liking and respecting yourself. People with high self-esteem are comfortable with their unique identities. They know their own strengths and weaknesses. They are proud of who they are.

Authorities say that teens have lower self-esteem than any other age group. Many teens wish they were more popular or better-looking. They have little self-confidence. They wish they were anything—but themselves.

Looks That Kill

Many teens worry about looking good. They think that looking better will make them happier. Why? Beautiful people are often treated better by others. "Kids in school care about how you look," says 12-year-old Isabel Mendez. "They don't care who you are on the inside."

Some teens try to raise their self-esteem through extreme diets or drugs. They'll do anything to look better.

Girls sometimes think trendy diets will fix their problems. Experts say that 39 percent of girls in fifth to eighth grade are on a diet!

Some boys also have problems with body image. They think the solution is to bulk up. Too many teens take drugs to build muscles.

Diets and drugs aren't solutions. Diets can make you tense and tired. Drugs can damage your body and even kill you. ➤

Words to Know! **tense** nervous

Problem and Solution

1. **UNDERLINE** What are typical self-esteem problems for many teens?

2. **WRITE** Describe two ways in which some teens attempt to solve their self-esteem problems.

Attempt 1:

_____

_____

Attempt 2:

_____

_____

3. **WRITE** Are teens' self-esteem problems serious? Why or why not?

_____
_____
_____
_____
_____

CRITICAL READING
Analyze

WRITE In your experience, how does peer pressure affect teens' self-esteem?

_____
_____
_____
_____

Active Reading

UNDERLINE Find one way to build your own self-esteem.

VOCABULARY
Target Word

appreciate

ap•pre•ci•ate (verb)

Rate It: ① ② ③ ④

Meaning

to _____ and

_____ for something

Example

My friends' _____

_____

is something I **appreciate** about them.

React and Write

▶ **WRITE** What do you like best about yourself?

Summarize

In one or two sentences, summarize the topic and important details in "Three Secrets of Self-Esteem."

Strong on the Inside

What is the solution to low self-esteem? Try not to focus on things you don't like about yourself. Instead, learn to recognize and **appreciate** the person you are. It's a challenge, but it will work.

Also, remember that you are a teenager. Ask adults about their teen years. Chances are, they'll remember feeling low self-esteem, too. Your self-esteem will improve as you get older.

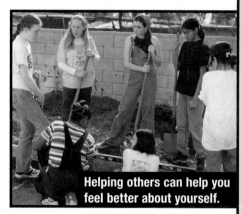
Helping others can help you feel better about yourself.

However, there are things you can do today to help yourself feel better. What are they? Check out these tips.

Three Secrets of Self-Esteem

1. Lend a hand. Doing things that benefit others can build your self-esteem and confidence. Do you enjoy spending time with kids or the elderly? Are you good with animals? Share your skills. Volunteering can give you a chance to shine.

2. Find a mentor. Look for someone who can give you good advice. Maybe it's a teacher, a coach, or an older relative. Mentors can help you understand and deal with your feelings.

3. Get involved. Find something you like to do. Join a school club. Try out for a sport. Convince your friends to do an activity you think might be fun. Being busy can be a good thing. If you focus on doing something fun, you'll stop focusing on your imperfections.

Lastly, just try to remember one important thing—you won't be a teen forever! (END)

| Words to Know! | **mentor** | someone who offers help and guidance |

Comprehension Focus
Problem and Solution

▶ Complete this chart with the problem, attempts, and solution in "The Secrets of Self-Esteem."

Problem

Attempt 1

Attempt 2

Solution

The Key Idea

WRITE What is this life skills feature mostly about?

_____

_____

VOCABULARY
Target Word

principle

prin•ci•ple (noun)

Rate It: ① ② ③ ④

Meaning

a basic _____

_____

Example

A *principle* I live by is:

_____

_____

_____

React and Write

WRITE What would you tell a friend who is being pressured to do something that will make his or her parents really angry?

The Power of PEER PRESSURE

Can you stand up to the crowd?

The Pressure to Fit In

Teens get pressure from all sides. They feel pressure to do well in school, to excel at a sport, or to look really good. But many teens say peer pressure is a serious challenge. It comes from wanting to fit in.

The pressure to fit in is most intense in middle school or junior high. During these years, teens begin to rebel against their families. They start making decisions for themselves. They start to search for **principles**, or beliefs, to live by.

For instance, a teen may decide that her principles include keeping physically fit and alcohol-free. Another teen's principles may involve being loyal to his friends before his family.

For many teens, friends become a *new* family. They join a group and begin to dress like their friends, act like their friends, and even think like their friends. Then the pressure is *really* on!

Experts recommend a solution. Teens need to figure out when peer pressure is healthy—and when it's not.

With Friends Like These . . .

Some teens will do stupid, dangerous things like shoplift or drink just to fit in. But teens aren't stupid. They know their behavior is dangerous. They know it can lead to big trouble. So, why do they do it? Because fitting in is more important than anything.

What are teens to do? First, they need to develop confidence about their values. They need a clear idea of who they are, and who they want to become. Then teens can begin to recognize those qualities in others. They can surround themselves with friends who pressure them in good ways, like joining a sports team. They can avoid friends who pressure them in negative ways, like doing drugs or cutting classes. ➤

Words to Know!	**recommend** to suggest a certain action

📖 Problem and Solution

1. **CIRCLE** When is the problem of peer pressure at its most intense?

2. **UNDERLINE** Why is peer pressure so intense during this time?

3. ▶ **WRITE** What solution do experts recommend for teens facing peer pressure?

_____

_____

4. ▶ **WRITE** What problems can come from the pressure to fit in?

_____

_____

REVIEW
📖 Summarize

Find the topic and key details in "With Friends Like These . . . " Then, summarize the section to a partner.

CRITICAL READING
🧠 Analyze

▶ **WRITE** What is the main difference between good and bad peer pressure?

_____

_____

_____

_____

_____

Active Reading

★**STAR** What is hazing?

 VOCABULARY
Target Word

participate

par•ti•ci•pate (verb)

Rate It: ① ② ③ ④

Meaning

to be _____ something

_____

Example

_____

_____

is an activity I often participate in.

 React and Write

▶ **WRITE** How do your friends influence you? Describe one good way and one bad way.

 Summarize

Summarize the topic and important details in the life skills feature "The Power of Peer Pressure."

Peer Pressure Gets Physical

Hazing is an extreme form of peer pressure. Hazing happens when teens want to join a group. Older teens in the group put the new members through really embarrassing situations. Hazing has become a big problem with clubs and school teams.

In 2003, 15 students in Chicago were charged with assault after a hazing. How did this happen? A group of senior girls invited a group of junior girls to play a football game. The game turned into a hazing. The seniors threw pig intestines and fish guts at the juniors. Girls were beaten, kicked, and choked. In the end, five girls had to be taken to the hospital. One girl had a broken foot and another needed 16 stitches in her head.

The incident was caught on video and shown on TV all over the country. The school expelled 33 seniors who **participated** in the hazing. Police charged 15 girls with battery, which is the legal term for attacking someone. One year later, 12 seniors pleaded guilty, and the rest of those charged were found guilty. They were sentenced to court supervision and community service.

Words to Know! | **reinforce** to make something stronger

TEXT FEATURE Reading a Bar Graph

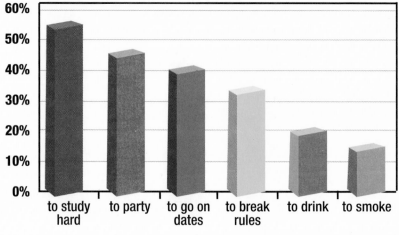

Teens Under Pressure
Percentage of teens who report pressure in six categories

A few of the juniors who suffered from the hazing hired a lawyer. They filed a 1.5 million dollar lawsuit against the girls who hazed them. The victims hoped that their lawsuit would make other people aware that hazing is a serious problem. They wanted to reinforce the message that hazing is wrong—and must be stopped.

Long-Term Solutions

Why is it so hard for teens to deal with unhealthy peer pressure like hazing? One problem teens have is that they focus on the short term. For example, a teen may feel pressure from friends to smoke. In the short term, smoking might seem like a solution. But it's not. Smoking can turn into a long-term problem. It is unhealthy and a hard habit to quit.

A better solution is to think about life in the long term. The next time you are about to do something you may regret, like shoplifting, think in the long term— that stealing is not worth getting a criminal record.

Finally, experts remind teens that peer pressure doesn't last forever. If you can survive Grades 6–8, then you've made it past the hardest part. Until then, stay tough under the pressure! END

A bar graph shows how different pieces of information relate to each other.

❶ **Analyze:** What information does this bar graph show?

Ⓐ the kinds of teens who feel peer pressure

Ⓑ the exact amount of peer pressure a teen feels

Ⓒ the percentage of teens who feel different types of pressure

❷ What color bar represents the percentage of teens who feel pressured to smoke?

Ⓐ green   Ⓑ blue   Ⓒ orange   Ⓓ yellow

❸ About how many teens report feeling pressure from peers to go on dates? _____

📖 Problem and Solution

1. CIRCLE How do teens get involved in hazing?

2. ▶ WRITE What are two problems that hazing can cause?

- _____
  _____

- _____
  _____

CRITICAL READING
🧠 Evaluate

▶ WRITE Should hazing be considered a crime? Why or why not? Use details from the reading in your response.

_____

_____

_____

_____

✓ Skills Check

1. ▶ WRITE What is one example of a problem that short-term thinking can cause?

_____

_____

_____

2. **UNDERLINE** Identify an example of how long-term thinking is a better solution.

Word Challenge

START

1 Identify them. What would give you a **negative** image at your school?

- [ ] cheating on a final test
- [ ] making fun of other kids
- [ ] riding the school bus
- [ ] wearing ripped-up jeans
- [ ] carrying a skateboard

2 Homophones

Homophones are words that sound alike but have different meanings and spellings. Examples are *peace* and *piece*, or *weight* and *wait*.

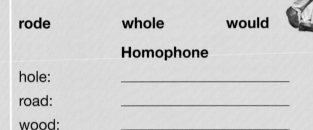

I have one guiding **principle**: always be cool in front of the **principal**.

Match each word to its homophone below.

rode   whole   would

Homophone

hole: _____

road: _____

wood: _____

Complete the sentence with two homophones.

I was able to _____ my old _____ phone, and buy a new one that takes pictures!

3 Choose them. Which **principles** do you agree with?

- [ ] Family comes first.
- [ ] Never turn your back on a friend.
- [ ] Honesty is always the best policy.
- [ ] Don't trust anyone.

5 Check them. Your friends could probably **convince** you to:

- [ ] ask someone out on a date.
- [ ] tell a lie.
- [ ] jump off a cliff.
- [ ] eat a bug.

4 Finish them. Complete these sentences.

A coach is an **authority** on

_____.

A doctor is an **authority** on

_____.

A DJ is an **authority** on

_____.

6 **Tell about yourself.** People can **rebel** in many different ways. Would you ever **rebel** by:

☐ staying out past curfew?

☐ talking to someone whom no one else talks to?

☐ listening to music no one else likes?

☐ wearing strange clothes?

7 **Reflect.** It's your birthday. List three gifts you would really **appreciate** getting.

1. _____

_____

2. _____

_____

3. _____

_____

8 **Finish them.** Complete each sentence with **constant** or **pressure**.

If you have no **confidence** talking in front of a group, you might feel a lot of _____ in speech class. Having to make speeches would give you _____ stress.

9 Compound Words

A **compound word** is made up of two or more smaller words. For example:

count + down = *countdown*

Draw a line to break each compound word into two words.

breakdown   downstairs   headache

homework   classmate   bookend

Use three of the compound words above to complete the sentences below.

The band was playing _____ in the basement. They played as loud as they wanted all night. This morning, I have a big

_____. If this keeps up,

I'm going to have a nervous _____!

COUNTDOWN: 10 - 9 - 8 - 7 - 6 - 5 - 4 - 3 - 2 - 1 - BLASTOFF!

10 **Explain.** You have to **participate** in the school talent show. What's your act?

_____

_____

_____

_____

FINISH

Writing Text Type

Argument Essay

An **argument essay** states a position or claim about an issue. The writer supports the claim with convincing evidence and reasons.

Read student Ana Baca's argument about the worst problem teenagers face today.

Student Model

Introduction

An **introductory statement** introduces the issue.

1. **UNDERLINE** the introductory statement.

A clear **thesis statement** presents the writer's claim about the issue.

2. **BOX** the thesis statement.

Body

Each body paragraph starts with a **topic sentence** that supports the writer's claim.

3. **UNDERLINE** the topic sentence in each paragraph.

Convincing reasons and relevant evidence support the argument.

4. ✔**CHECK** six reasons or pieces of evidence in the essay.

A strong argument points out weaknesses in **opposing arguments**.

5. →**PUT AN ARROW** next to one opposing argument.

Language Use

Transition words and phrases introduce or connect ideas.

6. **CIRCLE** four transitions.

Conclusion

The **conclusion** restates the thesis and offers a recommendation.

7. ★**STAR** the conclusion.

Banish Bullying!
by Ana Baca

Today's teens face many challenges. I believe that the worst problem teenagers face today is bullying. Bullying, in any of its forms, can hurt people. In extreme cases, bullying can even ruin lives.

Name-calling and physical bullying can make some teens so miserable that they avoid school. These teens may end up doing poorly, which can harm their future. Another form of bullying that hurts teens is cyber-bullying. Even though bullying on the Internet is not face-to-face, it can have a terrible effect on teens. The bullied person gets hurt, and the bully can get in trouble with the authorities.

Some people believe bullying is not a serious problem. They claim that bullying is just a normal part of growing up. However, something that causes so much harm should not be considered "normal."

In conclusion, bullying is a major problem for all teens. Bullying can have a negative effect on the victim and on the bully. I urge parents and educators to enforce tough policies against bullying.

Analyze the Text Type

▶ **Work with a partner to understand the purpose and form of an argument essay.**

Purpose: Argument Essay

The purpose of an argument essay is _____
_____

Introduction

The **introductory paragraph** of an argument essay includes:

1. an _____ that introduces the issue.

2. a thesis statement that presents the _____ about the issue.

Student Model | In her introduction, Baca:

1. states the issue she will discuss, which is: _____

2. presents her claim about the issue, which is: _____
_____

Body

The **body** provides **reasons and evidence** that support the writer's claim.

1. Each body paragraph starts with a _____

2. _____ support the topic sentence.

3. The writer points out _____ in the opposing arguments.

Student Model

1. The topic sentence in the first body paragraph is: _____
_____

2. One convincing reason or relevant evidence is: _____
_____

3. One opposing argument is: _____
_____

Conclusion

The **conclusion** restates the _____ and offers a _____

Student Model | Baca's recommendation is: _____
_____

Brainstorm

▶ Read the writing prompt. Then use the boxes to help you brainstorm your ideas about an issue.

Problems With Friendships

Problems in School

Writing Prompt:
Write an argument essay about the worst problem teenagers face today.

Problems With Self-Esteem

Problems Outside of School

State Your Position

▶ Select an idea from the idea web to help you determine your position.

I will argue that the worst problem teens face is _____

because _____

_____

Organize Ideas for Writing

▶ **Complete this outline with notes for your argument essay.**

I. Introduction Introduce the issue and your claim about it.

    A. Issue: _____

    B. Claim: _____

    _____

II. Body Write a topic sentence for each body paragraph that supports your claim. Then list two reasons or pieces of evidence to support the topic sentence. Use one of your topic sentences to address an opposing argument.

    A. Topic Sentence 1: _____

    _____

        Evidence/Reason: _____

        _____

        Evidence/Reason: _____

        _____

    B. Topic Sentence 2: _____

    _____

        Evidence/Reason: _____

        _____

        Evidence/Reason: _____

        _____

III. Conclusion Restate your thesis and make a recommendation.

    In summary, I believe _____

    _____

    Therefore, I recommend _____

    _____

    _____

    _____

    _____

Write Your Draft

▶ **Write a draft of your argument essay.**

Writing Prompt:
Write an argument about the worst problem teenagers face today.

WORD CHOICES	
Everyday	**Precise**
big	major
bad	negative
need	require
say	argue, claim

_____
(title of essay)

Introduction

▶ **Write your introductory statement.**

I believe the worst problem teenagers face today is _____
(issue)

▶ **Write your thesis statement or plan.**

_____ is the worst problem for teens
(issue)

because _____
(claim)

_____

_____

_____

▶ **Type your introduction on the computer or write it on paper. Then use these transition words and phrases to help you complete a draft of your argument essay.**

Body

First of all, . . .	_For instance, . . ._
It is important to note that . . .	_Although some people claim that . . ._
In addition, . . .	_This is a false claim because . . ._
Consequently, . . .	_However, . . ._

Conclusion

In the end, . . .	_It is worth thinking about . . ._
In conclusion, . . .	_I recommend . . ._

Revise Your Essay

► **Evaluate:** Rate your argument essay. Then have a partner rate it.

Scoring Guide

needs improvement	average	good	excellent
1	2	3	4

1. **UNDERLINE** the introductory statement. Does it introduce the issue effectively?

   Self   1   2   3   4
   Partner   1   2   3   4

2. **BOX** the thesis statement. Does it present a claim effectively?

   Self   1   2   3   4
   Partner   1   2   3   4

3. **UNDERLINE** the topic sentence in each body paragraph. Does each one support the claim?

   Self   1   2   3   4
   Partner   1   2   3   4

4. ✔**CHECK** reasons and evidence. Are they convincing and relevant?

   Self   1   2   3   4
   Partner   1   2   3   4

5. →**PUT AN ARROW** next to an opposing argument. Does the essay point out a weakness?

   Self   1   2   3   4
   Partner   1   2   3   4

6. **CIRCLE** transition words and phrases. Do they connect ideas?

   Self   1   2   3   4
   Partner   1   2   3   4

7. ★**STAR** the conclusion. Does it offer a recommendation?

   Self   1   2   3   4
   Partner   1   2   3   4

► **Discuss:** Give feedback on your partner's argument essay.

1. Start with positive comments about your partner's argument essay.

   You did an effective job of _____

   _____

   You support your claim by _____

   _____

2. Give your partner suggestions for revision.

   This essay would be clearer if _____

   _____

   Your claim would be stronger if you ____

   _____

   _____

   To support this point better, you could

   _____

   _____

3. Answer any questions your partner has about your suggestions.

4. Ask your partner for feedback. Use the frames below to summarize your partner's feedback.

   I did an effective job of . . .
   A strong part of my argument is . . .
   You had a question about . . .
   Two changes I need to make are . . .

► **Revise** Now revise your argument essay.

Grammar USING IRREGULAR VERBS

Most past-tense verbs end in -ed. **Irregular verbs** do not.

- You must remember the different spellings of irregular past-tense verbs.
- The verb *to be* is a common irregular verb. Its **present-tense** forms are I am, you are, he/she is. Its past-tense forms are I was, you were, he was.

Example

Present-Tense Verb	Past-Tense Verb
I **am** sorry for my actions.	I was sorry for my actions.
Amy **sends** out cards for birthdays.	She sent one to me last week.
They usually **eat** lunch at noon.	Yesterday, they ate lunch early.

▶ **Circle the correct past-tense verb in each sentence below.**

1. Carlos once [did done] mean things to get approval.
2. He even got [catched caught] participating in a hazing.
3. Carlos's parents [made maked] the decision to talk to his teachers.
4. The teachers [was were] worried about him.
5. After they spoke with Carlos, he [was were] nicer to everyone.
6. Carlos [finded found] a way to improve his self-esteem.

▶ **Rewrite the sentences below using the past-tense form of the verb.**

7. Eric **fall** off the train and died.

_____

8. His girlfriend **tell** him not to climb outside the train.

_____

9. His uncle **says** that peer pressure caused Eric's death.

_____

10. The accident **make** many teens stop and think.

_____

▶ **Edit Your Draft.** Look at the sentences in your draft. **Do all sentences use the correct verb forms?** Fix the ones that do not.

Mechanics USING COMMAS WITH INTRODUCTORY WORDS

A **comma** follows an opening word or phrase at the beginning of a sentence.

- *Yes*, *No*, *Next*, and *Later* are examples of opening words.
- *In addition* and *After a while* are examples of opening phrases.

Example

Correct	Incorrect
Next, Kim began helping others.	Next Kim began helping others.
After a while, she felt better.	After a while she felt better.

▶ **Find and correct five errors in this paragraph.**

Student Model

CHECK AND CORRECT

- ☐ **UNDERLINE** one verb-tense error and correct it.
- ☐ Insert two missing commas.
- ☐ (CIRCLE) two spelling errors and correct them.

   I think teens today have too much free time, and this leads to boredum. Boredom is the worst problem for teens today. It leads to dangerous habits, such as smoking. True there are other serious challenges for teens. However, research shows that teens who are involved in activities such as sports are more likely to stay out of trouble. One teen reported that when he join the basketball team, his self-steem improved. In addition he made new friends.

▶ **Edit Your Draft.** Look at the sentences in your draft. **Are opening phrases and words followed by commas?** Fix the ones that are not.

Final Draft/Present

▶ **Write a final draft of your essay on the computer or on paper. Check it again and correct any errors before you present it.**

Focus Skill Protect Yourself on the Internet

Evaluate a Social Networking Account

A social networking account helps people share information and stay in touch with friends online. The account's privacy settings help protect the social network user.

▶ **Read the privacy settings for the social networking account below. Then answer the questions.**

MARK IT

- **UNDERLINE** the name of the person who uses this account.

- ⬭ **CIRCLE** the number of friends he has.

- ★ **STAR** the information that he allows everyone to see.

SOCIALNET

Jack Watson

Friends 1,032

Privacy Settings

First and Last Name	Everyone
Birthday	Everyone
Hometown	Everyone
Religious and Political Views	Everyone
Emails	Only Friends
Status Updates	Only Friends
Photos	Only Friends
Videos	Only Friends
Links	Everyone

---

① What kind of information does Jack let only his friends see?

Ⓐ his name and birthday

Ⓑ his name, photos, and videos

Ⓒ his emails and status updates

Ⓓ his religious and political views

② What information could a stranger use to find where Jack lives?

Ⓐ his name, birthday, and hometown

Ⓑ his religious views and status updates

Ⓒ his emails and political views

Ⓓ his photos and videos

③ Is Jack taking a risk by using this privacy setting? Why or why not?

_____

_____

_____

_____

_____

What could Jack do differently?

_____

_____

_____

_____

School Counselor
Lynn Washington

This school counselor helps students with life and school issues.

▶ **Read the interview and job information. Then answer the questions below about Lynn Washington's job.**

S Scholastic: How do you help students deal with peer pressure?

Lynn Washington: Once, I had a student who was being pressured to cheat. Her classmates wanted to copy her homework. She came to me, and we practiced ways to say "no."

S What's the hardest part of your job?

It's hard when students struggle because they don't have what they need. One student was living in a car with his mother and two brothers. His grades started to fall, and I found out why. His mom told him not to tell anyone that they were homeless. She was afraid her kids would be taken away. I talked to the mom, and got the family the help that they needed.

S What's the best part of your job?

I love to see students succeed and know that I had a part in it. I really get attached to all the students I work with. I have a group from each year that I still keep in touch with.

❶ **How do you think Lynn Washington would help a student who was facing peer pressure online?**

_____

_____

_____

❷ **How difficult is Washington's job? Mark the line.**

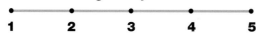

1   2   3   4   5
Not very difficult   Very difficult

❸ **I think Washington's job is/isn't (circle one) difficult because**

_____

_____

ON THE JOB

LOCATION
Silver Spring, Maryland

EDUCATION
Bachelor's degree; Master's degree in School Counseling

RESPONSIBILITIES
- Plans activities, such as role playing to help students
- Listens to students' problems
- Helps students solve personal and academic problems

SKILLS
- Listening to people
- Solving problems
- Collaborating with teachers and parents

SALARY
$48,000–$60,000

SURPRISING PART OF WORK
"I think about my job late at night. I'm either planning activities or worrying about a student who has a problem."

CAREER CONNECTION

Education and Training
www.careerclusters.org
....
Related Jobs
- teacher
- psychologist
- teacher's aide

Are social networks harmful for teens?

Do social networks help or hurt? Hold a class debate in which one side argues that social networks are beneficial, while the other side argues that social networks are harmful.

1 **State your position.** Which side of the debate are you on?

Social networks are/are not (circle one) harmful for teens.

2 **Consider multiple perspectives.** Based on what you've learned in this Workshop and in your own experience, what are some benefits and challenges with social networks?

Benefits	Challenges

3 **Justify your position.** What details about social networks and teens support your position? Give specific facts and examples.

Our Arguments	Our Support
a.	
b.	
c.	

AN EFFECTIVE DEBATE

✓ states both sides of the issue.

✓ provides examples, facts, and anecdotes to support your team's position.

✓ responds effectively to the other team's arguments.

④ **Prepare notes for your debate.** Organize your points. Then think ahead: How might the other side respond to your arguments?

DEBATE: _Are social networks harmful for teens?_

OPENING STATEMENT: _____

_____

_____

_____

_____

_____

OUR ARGUMENT:

a. _____

_____

_____

b. _____

_____

_____

c. _____

_____

_____

POSSIBLE RESPONSE:

a. _____

_____

_____

_____

b. _____

_____

_____

_____

c. _____

_____

_____

SUMMARY/CLOSING STATEMENT: _____

_____

_____

_____

Comprehension

▶ **Fill in the circle next to the correct answer.**

1. In the article about Eric Alvarez, what was Eric's main problem?

   Ⓐ He argued too much with his aunt.

   Ⓑ He was scared of riding the subway.

   Ⓒ He was pressured by his friends to do crazy stunts.

   Ⓓ He took drugs because he had low self-esteem.

> **Here's a Tip.**
> You can answer some questions by looking directly in the text. For other questions, you have to combine what you already know with what you've read.

2. Why are extreme diets and drugs *not* effective solutions to low self-esteem?

   Ⓐ Extreme diets and drugs can damage your health.

   Ⓑ You are either born with self-esteem, or you'll never have it.

   Ⓒ Only doctors can help with low self-esteem.

   Ⓓ Students who diet or use drugs are teased.

CRITICAL READING

3. Evaluate: Which is an effective way to build self-esteem?

   Ⓐ Brag to other people about what you're good at.

   Ⓑ Tutor a younger student in a subject you're good at.

   Ⓒ Hide from other people until your teen years pass.

   Ⓓ Hang out with people who like to rebel.

CRITICAL READING

4. Evaluate: Peer pressure is healthy when _____.

   Ⓐ it gets your family upset or worried about you

   Ⓑ you take dangerous risks to please your friends

   Ⓒ it makes you treat your friends badly

   Ⓓ it gives you a clear idea of your principles

5. Why do teenagers get involved in dangerous hazing?

   Ⓐ They want to be better-looking.

   Ⓑ They want to impress their parents and teachers.

   Ⓒ They want to fit in with a group.

   Ⓓ They want to stand out from the crowd.

Vocabulary

► **Fill in the circle next to the correct definitions of the underlined words.**

1. Authorities say that good self-esteem helps teens to deal with peer pressure.

   Ⓐ psychologists; happiness
   Ⓑ experts; force
   Ⓒ teachers; project
   Ⓓ parents; chore

2. Tianna convinced Rushawn to join her at the school dance, even though he was shy.

   Ⓐ invited along with other people
   Ⓑ counted
   Ⓒ made someone believe or do something
   Ⓓ allowed

3. After cheating to win the class election, Saria got a negative image at school.

   Ⓐ bad
   Ⓑ happy
   Ⓒ unhappy
   Ⓓ total

► **Fill in the circle next to the correct answer.**

4. Which two words are homophones?

   Ⓐ gum/gym
   Ⓑ principal/principle
   Ⓒ back/crack
   Ⓓ care/car

5. Which is a compound word?

   Ⓐ picture
   Ⓑ gigantic
   Ⓒ breakdown
   Ⓓ computer

Short Answer

CRITICAL READING

► **Analyze: Use what you've read in this Workshop to answer the question. Check your spelling and grammar.**

What is an example of peer pressure at your school?

_____

_____

_____

_____

COMPREHENSION FOCUS
Story Elements

CRITICAL READING FOCUS
Synthesize
Evaluate

Reading 1 The Fall of the House of Usher |
Short Story

Reading 2 from "The Haunted House" | **Poetry**

POE:

The Master of Horror

Meet the master of horror, Edgar Allan Poe. He lived from 1809 to 1849. His life was as mysterious as the stories he wrote. At age 40, Poe was found lying barely conscious in a street. Four days later he died, poor and almost unknown.

During his short, sad life, Poe wrote some of the scariest stories ever written. You are about to read one of them!

Academic Vocabulary

◎ Target Word	Meaning	Examples
▶ Read the Target Words. Rate each one using the scale below.*	▶ Read the Target Word meanings. Write in the missing words.	▶ Finish the Target Word examples below. Write in the missing ones.
despair (p. 151) de•spair (noun) ① ② ③ ④	a feeling of being _____ and having no hope	• The family felt complete **despair** when _____ _____ • If _____ I would feel **despair**.
peculiar (p. 151) pe•cu•liar (adjective) ① ② ③ ④	strange	• I think it's **peculiar** when _____ _____ • _____ _____
generation (p. 151) gen•er•a•tion (noun) ① ② ③ ④	all of the people of about the same _____ in a family	• _____ are part of my **generation**. • People from my _____ **generation** have old-fashioned beliefs.
anxiety (p. 153) anx•i•e•ty (noun) ① ② ③ ④	a strong feeling of _____	The thought of snakes fills her with **anxiety**.
utter (p. 157) ut•ter (verb) ① ② ③ ④	to speak or make a sound from your mouth	• Words I might **utter** in fear are _____ • _____ _____

*Rating Scale
① = I don't know the word.   **③** = I think I know the word.
② = I've seen it or heard it.   **④** = I know it and use it.

Comprehension Focus

Story Elements

A **short story** like "The Fall of the House of Usher" is a brief work of literary fiction. To understand a short story, consider these elements:

1. Setting is where and when the story takes place. This story takes place in a strange old house a long time ago.

2. Characters are the people in the story.

Usher, a man who lives in an old house

the narrator, a friend of Usher's

Madeline, Usher's sister

3. Plot is the sequence of events in a story. The plot contains a problem that the main character needs to solve. In "The Fall of the House of Usher," the main character helps an old friend, Roderick Usher. But will he be able to handle Usher's illness—and his strange house?

4. Theme is an important message about life that the author wants readers to understand. A story can have more than one theme. In this story, one theme is: Isolating yourself away from the world can cause mental problems.

▶ **Turn the page and start reading to find out what happens to the House of Usher.**

The Fall of the House of Usher

▶ **Complete this chart as you reread the story.**

	Part 1 (pp. 150–151)	**Part 2** (pp. 152–155)	**Part 3** (pp. 156–157)
Setting	Time: *a gloomy autumn day* Place: *outside the old mansion*	Time: Place:	Time: Place:
Character	Who is the main character? Describe him/her:	How does the character change?	What is the character like now?
Plot Events	What happens at the beginning of the story?	What happens in the middle of the story?	How does the story end?
Theme	Author's message:		

Active Reading

 ★**STAR** What does Usher ask the narrator to do?

VOCABULARY
 Target Word

depressing

de•press•ing (adjective)

Rate It: ① ② ③ ④

Meaning

making you feel _____

Example

*A movie is **depressing** when _____ _____*

 Craft and Structure

Mood is the general feeling an author creates. The author chooses specific words and phrases to create the feeling.

1. ▶ **WRITE** What is the mood of this story?

_____

_____

2. ✔ **CHECK** Mark three words or phrases that help to create the mood of this story.

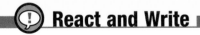 **React and Write**

▶ **WRITE** If you were Usher's friend, would you go to his house to help him? Why or why not?

The Fall of the House of Usher

adapted from the story by Edgar Allan Poe

A letter arrived from my boyhood friend, Roderick Usher. He begged me to come visit him at his family house. Usher said that he was ill in both his body and mind. I could tell from his words that he was not well.

"You are my best and only friend," Usher wrote. "Perhaps you can ease my suffering by coming to stay with me a few weeks."

Usher's words disturbed me, because even though we had been companions since childhood, there was always a side of him I felt I didn't know. And I had heard many rumors about his strange family. Yet, as his friend, I felt obliged to obey his request.

I set out for Usher's house on a gloomy autumn day. As I came upon the ancient mansion, I sensed an atmosphere of decay. The stone walls of the house were crumbling, and the windows stared down at me like vacant eyes. Surrounding the house were dead bushes, rotting tree trunks, and a dark moat filled with sluggish water. My eyes fixed on a long crack that

| Words to Know! | **vacant** | empty |

zigzagged down the front of the house like an open wound. The place was more than **depressing**—it was terrifying. A deep sense of despair crept over me.

The house had been in Usher's family for hundreds of years. The family was known for their artistic and musical talents, but there was something peculiar about them; not one member of the family ever moved out of the House of Usher. Generation after generation of Ushers had lived—and died—there.

Reluctantly, I urged my horse forward across the creaky bridge that spanned the moat. For a moment, I imagined that I was crossing into hell.

A servant gestured me inside the mansion, then led me down dark passages and up a staircase cloaked in shadows. Finally, I arrived at Usher's room.

Inside the room, the narrow, pointed windows were covered with blood-red draperies. The furniture was in tatters. Roderick Usher rose from a sofa to greet me. ➤

Story Elements

Setting

1. ▶ **WRITE** What words would you use to describe Usher's house?

_____

_____

Character

2. **UNDERLINE** Mark a detail that describes Usher.

3. **UNDERLINE** Mark a detail that describes how the narrator is feeling.

Plot

4. ▶ **WRITE** What has happened in the story so far?

_____

_____

_____

_____

_____

_____

_____

Theme

5. **CIRCLE** A theme of this story is: "Isolating yourself from the world can cause mental problems." Identify one detail that supports this theme.

▶ **Now go to page 149. Add details to Part 1 of the chart.**

Active Reading

★STAR What does Usher say is wrong with him?

VOCABULARY

Target Word

mental

men•tal *(adjective)*

Rate It: ① ② ③ ④

Meaning

having to do with _____

Example

A _____

has great *mental* abilities.

CRITICAL READING
Evaluate

▶ **WRITE** Do you think Usher truly does suffer from a mental disease? Why or why not?

_____

_____

_____

_____

React and Write

▶ **WRITE** If you were the narrator and just saw Madeline, what would you think of her?

I couldn't believe my eyes as I gazed upon his face. My old friend was terribly altered from when I had last seen him. His eyes were watery and strangely enlarged, his lips seemed drained of color, his skin was as pale as a ghost's, and his hair floated wildly above his face.

Yet, when Usher greeted me, he reminded me of exactly how he had been as a boy. "So good to see you, friend. I'm very grateful that you came," Usher said. His words were warm and polite, yet his voice betrayed a nervous agitation.

Immediately, I asked him what the trouble was.

"I'm suffering from an evil family **mental** disease," he said. "I will perish from it, I know. My physicians say there is no cure." I asked him to describe the symptoms of the disease.

Words to Know! | **agitation** anxiety, nervousness, or worry

"I can barely eat," Usher said, "and I am fearful of straying away from the house. Sudden lights and noises disturb me. Everything, it seems, fills me with an overwhelming terror."

"What can I do to help you?" I asked.

"Sit, sit. Make yourself comfortable," said Usher. But comfort was not possible in that house. The sudden gusts of wind that blew through its shadowy walls sent a chill down my spine and through my heart.

Usher continued his story. He had not left the old mansion for many years because its gloom had influenced his mind, filling him with anxiety. Much of that anxiety was for his beloved sister, Madeline. She was his only living relative, but she too was afflicted by a peculiar disease.

"Her body and mind are wasting away," he explained. "If she died, I would be the last of the ancient race of Ushers."

As he spoke, I sensed a presence in the room. I glanced around and saw Madeline passing through the shadows. She disappeared into the darkness without speaking a word.

Usher buried his face in his hands and cried. "That will probably be the last time we see her alive," he said tragically. I decided not to mention her name again. This house—and its inhabitants—was beginning to play on my nerves.

For the next several days, I did everything in my power to lift Usher's spirits. We painted, read books, and I listened to him play melancholy music on his guitar. But never did we mention Madeline's name. ➤

Words to Know! **melancholy** sorrowful

Story Elements

Setting

1. ▶ **WRITE** How does the house affect Usher and the narrator?

_____
_____
_____
_____

Character

2. **UNDERLINE** Identify a detail that describes Madeline.

Plot

3. ▶ **WRITE** What does the narrator learn about Roderick and Madeline in this part of the story?

_____
_____
_____
_____
_____
_____

Theme

4. **CIRCLE** A theme of this story is: "Isolating yourself from the world can cause mental problems." Find two details about Usher to support this theme.

Active Reading

★**STAR** What do Usher and the narrator do with Madeline's body?

VOCABULARY

Target Word

bizarre

bi•zarre (adjective)

Rate It: ① ② ③ ④

Meaning

very _____

Example

An example of a **bizarre**
animal is _____

_____

CRITICAL READING

Synthesize

▶ **WRITE** What do you think is happening in the House of Usher?

_____

_____

_____

_____

_____

React and Write

▶ **WRITE** If Usher asked you to help put his sister in a dungeon vault, would you agree to do it? How would you feel?

For a while, I imagined that the gloom hanging over the House of Usher might lift, but I was wrong. Things were about to get much worse.

Usher's thoughts were growing more and more **bizarre**. One day he turned to me and asked, "Do you think the stone walls of this house are alive?"

I hesitated to answer, and stared at his wild eyes.

"They are alive," he said. "Look how each stone is arranged in the wall, like members of a family. These stones are alive indeed—unlike the lady Madeline, who is no more."

My heart froze, and I took a deep breath. Now Roderick Usher was the last of his family.

That evening, Usher asked me to help prepare his sister for burial in the family vault. Together, we laid her wasted-away body in an iron casket, then we carried the casket down to the vault, which lay deep under the house in a shadowy dungeon. This dungeon was right below the bedroom where I was sleeping.

Words to Know!	**vault** an underground chamber

Before sliding the casket lid shut, I glanced at Madeline. There was a great resemblance to her brother. "We were twins," Usher whispered tragically.

I couldn't bear to look at this dead woman any longer. I was filled with emotion as we screwed tight the lid of the casket. Then we shut the iron door of the vault, which made a sharp grating sound as it closed.

After seven nights had passed, Usher's illness grew even worse. I would encounter him roaming about the house with no purpose, and he would sit slumped in his chair staring for hours at nothing.

On the eighth night, a violent storm began to gather, and I could not sleep. I began to tremble from a sense of horror I had never felt before. Then I heard a light step on the stairs. It was Usher, carrying a lantern.

"Have you not seen it?" he asked. His eyes looked half-insane. "Stay, stay, you will see it."

He flung open the window, and the fury of the storm burst in, nearly lifting us off our feet.

"Leave it closed!" I cried, and slammed the window shut. ➤

Story Elements

Setting

1. CIRCLE Where in the house is the dungeon?

Character

2. **WRITE** Why do you think the narrator mentions where the dungeon is?

____

____

____

____

Plot

3. **WRITE** What important event happens in this part of the story?

____

____

▶ **Now go to page 149. Add details to Part 2 of the chart.**

Craft and Structure

A **symbol** is something in the story that has meaning in itself, but also stands for something else. Example, a heart may also stand for love.

WRITE In this story the House of Usher is a home, but it is also a symbol. What do you think it stands for?

____

____

💡 Active Reading

▶ **WRITE** What effect are the noises having on Usher?

_____

_____

◎ VOCABULARY
Target Word

remove

re•move (verb)

Rate It: ① ② ③ ④

Meaning

to take something _____

Example

Something I might **remove** *from my backpack is* _____

_____

❗ React and Write

▶ **WRITE** What would you have done if you had heard the peculiar rattle and screaming sound?

💬 Make Inferences

What do you think really happened to Madeline? Support your response with evidence from the story.

Usher and I sat down, exhausted with emotion. I decided we should read a story out loud, to help calm us down. I began to read, but paused when I heard something rattle.

It's just the wind, I told myself. I continued to read.

Then I heard the peculiar rattle again, followed by a sharp, grating, screaming sound from below us—from the dungeon.

Usher was facing away from me. Did he hear what I was hearing? I attempted to continue reading, but the clanging and the screaming grew ever worse.

Completely unnerved, I leapt to my feet and rushed to my friend's chair. I tapped on his shoulder, and when he turned to me, I saw a sickly smile quivering on his lips.

Words to Know!	**quivering**	shaking

"Yes, I hear it," he uttered. He almost seemed to be speaking to himself. "I hear it, and have heard it—for many long, long hours. Even for many days. Is she alive? Did we seal her in the casket while living? Oh, where will I escape? Is she coming? Are those her footsteps? Is that her heartbeat? Madman!"

Below us, a sharp, grating noise sounded as though a casket was **removing** itself from its place in the vault.

Usher cried out, "I don't know who is alive in this house and who is dead! Look, there she is!"

Suddenly, a strong gust of wind blew open the window and threw Usher to the floor. Outside, the figure of Madeline seemed to hover like a ghost. Then, with a low moan, Madeline's pale, blood-stained form fell upon her brother and bore him to the floor—a corpse.

I fled that house in terror and panic. The storm had grown in intensity, and for an instant, the night flashed bright with lightning. I looked up and saw that the moon was blood-red. I ran across the bridge, and then looked back. At that moment, I saw the walls of the mansion split along the zigzag crack. Then, the dark waters of the moat swallowed up the stones of the HOUSE OF USHER. ⟨END⟩

Meet the Author

EDGAR ALLAN POE
Born: 1809 in Boston, Massachusetts
Died: October 7, 1849

His Legacy: Poe is considered one of the greatest horror writers of all time. He wrote many poems and horror stories. He also invented the modern detective story. Two of his most famous stories are "The Tell-Tale Heart," written from the point of view of a murderer, and "The Cask of Amontillado," a creepy story about being buried alive.

 Story Elements

Setting
1. **CIRCLE** Where are the noises coming from?

Character
2. **UNDERLINE** Find what Usher fears he has done to Madeline.

Plot
3. **WRITE** How does the story end?

_____
_____
_____
_____

Theme
4. **WRITE** How does extreme isolation affect Usher and his family?

_____
_____

▶ Now go to page 149. Complete Part 3 of the chart and the theme.

Skills Check

1. **WRITE** How does the narrator try to help Usher?

_____
_____

2. **★STAR** How does the narrator feel at the end of the story?

Active Reading

★**STAR** Where is the haunted house located?

VOCABULARY
Target Word

linger

lin•ger (verb)

Rate It: ① ② ③ ④

Meaning

to _____ around

Example

A sports fan might **linger** after a game to _____

_____

CRITICAL READING
Synthesize

▶**WRITE** What is another example of a place that might cause anxiety and despair?

_____

_____

React and Write

▶**WRITE** What qualities would make a house scary to you?

---

from **THE HAUNTED**

by Jack Prelutsky

On a hilltop bleak and bare
looms the castle of despair,
only phantoms **linger** there
within its dismal walls.
Through the dark they're creeping, crawling,
frenzied furies battling, brawling,
sprawling, calling, caterwauling
through the dusky halls.

Filmy visions, ever flocking,
dart through chambers, crudely mocking,
rudely rapping, tapping, knocking
on the crumbling doors.
Tortured spirits whine and wail,
they grope and grasp, they wildly flail,
their hollow voices rasp and rail
beneath the moldering floors.

In the corners, eyes are gleaming,
everywhere are nightmares streaming,
diabolic horrors screaming
in the sombrous air.
So shun this place where specters soar—
it's you and you they're waiting for
to haunt your souls forevermore
in their castle of despair.

Words to Know! **sombrous** gloomy and depressing

HOUSE

Rhyme Two or more words rhyme when their ending syllables have the same or similar sounds.

▶ **WRITE** Find words at the ends of lines of the poem that rhyme with the words below.

bare: _____

wail: _____

gleaming: _____

Text Structure A stanza is a group of lines about one idea or topic. A stanza in a poem is like a paragraph in a story.

▶ **WRITE** How many stanzas are in this poem? How many lines are in each stanza?

_____

_____

Theme is an important message about life that the writer wants readers to understand. A theme in "The Fall of the House of Usher" is that extreme isolation can cause mental problems.

▶ **WRITE** How does this poem relate to that theme?

_____

_____

_____

_____

_____

WORD CHALLENGE

This movie is really **depressing**. I can't believe how **sad** it is.

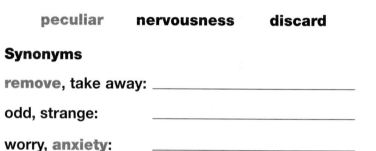

START

1 **Decide.** How much **anxiety** would each of the following give you? Rate them.

1 = least **anxiety**
4 = most **anxiety**

____ hearing a strange sound in the middle of the night

____ riding on a scary roller coaster

____ being locked in a room full of rats

____ walking through a graveyard at midnight

2 Synonyms

Synonyms are words that have similar meanings. Examples are *cold* and *chilly,* and *sleepy* and *drowsy*.

Match each word to its synonyms below.

peculiar   **nervousness**   **discard**

Synonyms

remove, take away: _____

odd, strange: _____

worry, **anxiety:**   _____

4 **Decide.** Which one of these sentences uses the word **uttered** correctly?

☐ He **uttered** the ball to the pitcher.

☐ He **uttered** his name to the teacher.

☐ He **uttered** over the puddle.

☐ He **uttered** the whole song.

3 **Describe it.** What are two things that make *your* **generation** different from your parents' **generation**?

• _____
  _____

• _____
  _____

5 **Tell.** What's the most **depressing** movie you have ever seen?

_____
_____
_____

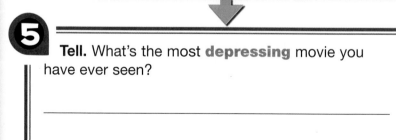

8 Word Families

A **word family** is a group of words that share the same base word and have related meanings, such as *terror, terrify,* and *terrorize*. *Terror* is a feeling of fear. *Terrify* and *terrorize* mean to make someone afraid.

Okay. I know! I'm really **anxious** about this test. I'm feeling a lot of **anxiety**.

Finish them. Complete each sentence with the correct form of the word *terror*.

1. I don't want to watch this bizarre movie. It will

_____ me.

2. Don't _____ your little brother!

3. The _____ of the hurricane was finally over.

6

Tell about it. Finish this **bizarre** sentence.

I thought it was **bizarre** when the huge blue dog

_____

_____

_____

_____

7

Check it. Which are easy **mental** exercises for you?

☐ doing multiplication

☐ thinking of a funny joke

☐ remembering a phone number

☐ memorizing dates for a test

*Coming up with great jokes is an easy **mental** exercise for me.*

9

Check it. Which of the following would fill you with **despair**?

☐ a bad haircut

☐ a hard test

☐ having to **remove** a bandage

☐ having to eat vegetables

Don't despair. It will grow back.

10

Think about it. Finish the sentences.

If I **linger** in the school hallway for too long, _____

_____

An odor that might **linger** around the house for a long time is _____

_____

FINISH

Writing Text Type
Literary Analysis

A **literary analysis** carefully examines a text, or one element of a text, such as character, plot, setting, or theme in a story.

▶ **Read student Juan Morales's analysis of theme in "The Fall of the House of Usher."**

Introduction

An **introductory statement** identifies the title, author, and text type that the writer will analyze.

1. **UNDERLINE** the introductory statement.

A **thesis statement** presents a plan for the essay.

2. **BOX** the thesis statement.

Body

Each **body paragraph** starts with a **topic sentence** that includes a controlling idea.

3. **UNDERLINE** the topic sentence in each body paragraph.

Evidence from the text supports the writer's analysis.

4. ✔ **CHECK** two pieces of evidence in each paragraph.

Direct quotations from the text provide evidence for the analysis.

5. **DOUBLE UNDERLINE** two direct quotations.

Language Use

Transition words and phrases connect ideas.

6. **CIRCLE** five transitions.

Conclusion

The **conclusion** sums up the writer's ideas about the text.

7. ★ **STAR** the conclusion.

Student Model

A True and Loyal Friend
by Juan Morales

In the short story "The Fall of the House of Usher" by Edgar Allan Poe, one significant theme is that true friends try to help you no matter what.

One example is when the narrator goes to visit Usher, his friend in need. The narrator has heard strange things about Usher's family, but he feels "obliged to obey his request" (150). A true friend, he puts aside his concerns, and goes to Usher's house.

At the house, the narrator tries "to lift Usher's spirits," though the house is causing him anxiety (153). He also helps Usher to bury his sister Madeline, who appears to be dead. This is a task only a loyal friend would help with.

In these ways, the narrator shows that he is a true friend. He does all he can to help the troubled Usher, even when it troubles him to do so.

Analyze the Text Type

▶ **Work with a partner to understand the purpose and form of a literary analysis.**

Purpose: Literary Analysis

The purpose of a literary analysis is _____
_____

Introduction

The **introductory paragraph** of a literary analysis includes:

1. an _____ that identifies what text will be analyzed.
2. a thesis statement that _____ for the essay.

Student Model | In his introduction, Morales:

1. states the text type, title, and author of the text he will analyze, which is:
_____

2. states his thesis, which is: _____
_____

Body

The **body paragraphs** provide evidence that supports the thesis.

1. The body paragraph starts with a _____
2. The rest of the sentences give _____ that support the thesis.

Student Model

1. The topic sentence in the first body paragraph is: _____
_____

2. List two details Morales includes in the first body paragraph.
- _____
- _____

Conclusion

The **conclusion** _____ the writer's ideas about the _____

Student Model | Morales concludes his analysis by saying _____
_____

Brainstorm

▶ Read the writing prompt. Then use the boxes to identify ideas and details from the text you will analyze.

Character

Plot

Writing Prompt:
Analyze character, plot, setting, or theme in "The Fall of the House of Usher."

Setting

Theme

Choose Your Topic

▶ Select one of your ideas from the idea web. Then complete the sentences below.

I plan to analyze _____

In this story, _____

_____

Organize Ideas for Writing

▶ Complete this outline with notes for your literary analysis of "The Fall of the House of Usher."

I. Introduction List details about the text you will analyze.

A. Text Type: _____

B. Title: _____

C. Author: _____

D. Story Element: _____

E. My Thesis Statement: _____

_____

II. Body Write a topic sentence for each body paragraph. Then list two details from the text that support the topic sentence.

A. Topic Sentence 1: _____

_____

Detail 1: _____

_____

Detail 2: _____

_____

B. Topic Sentence 2: _____

_____

Detail 1: _____

_____

Detail 2: _____

_____

III. Conclusion In one or two sentences, sum up your ideas about the text.

In summary, _____

_____

_____

_____

Write Your Draft

▶ **Write a draft of your literary analysis.**

Writing Prompt:
Analyze character, plot, setting, or theme in "The Fall of the House of Usher."

WORD CHOICES	
Everyday	**Precise**
makes	creates
big	vast, enormous
fall apart	collapse
alone	isolated

_____
(title of analysis)

Introduction

▶ **Write your introductory statement.**

In the _____
(text type and title)

by_____, the author_____
(author's name)   (general statement)

_____

▶ **Write your thesis statement.**

The story's _____ is _____
(story element)   (controlling idea)

_____

▶ **Type your introductory paragraph on the computer or write it on paper. Then use these transition words and phrases to help you complete a draft of your literary analysis.**

Body

The story takes place in . . .	_The author creates . . ._
In this story, . . .	_For instance, . . ._
Furthermore, . . .	_The character shows . . ._

Conclusion

Overall, . . .	_In summary, . . ._
In conclusion, . . .	_The story's theme . . ._

Revise Your Essay

▶ **Evaluate:** Rate your analysis. Then have a writing partner rate it.

Scoring Guide

needs improvement	average	good	excellent
1	2	3	4

1. UNDERLINE the introductory statement. Does it identify the title, author, and text type?

Self　1　2　3　4
Partner　1　2　3　4

2. BOX the thesis statement. Does it present a plan for the essay?

Self　1　2　3　4
Partner　1　2　3　4

3. UNDERLINE the topic sentence in each body paragraph. Does each include a controlling idea?

Self　1　2　3　4
Partner　1　2　3　4

4. ✔CHECK the evidence. Does the evidence support the analysis?

Self　1　2　3　4
Partner　1　2　3　4

5. DOUBLE UNDERLINE the direct quotations. Do they provide evidence for the analysis?

Self　1　2　3　4
Partner　1　2　3　4

6. CIRCLE the transition words and phrases. Do they connect ideas?

Self　1　2　3　4
Partner　1　2　3　4

7. ★STAR the conclusion. Does it sum up the writer's ideas?

Self　1　2　3　4
Partner　1　2　3　4

▶ **Discuss:** Give feedback on your partner's literary analysis.

1. Start with positive comments about your partner's literary analysis.

You did an effective job of _____

_____

I appreciate the way you _____

_____

2. Give your partner suggestions for revision.

I have a question about _____

_____

Your thesis statement needs _____

_____

The evidence would be stronger if _____

_____

_____

3. Answer any questions your partner has about your suggestions.

4. Ask your partner for feedback. Use the frames below to summarize your partner's feedback.

I did an effective job of . . .
You appreciated the way I . . .
You had a question about . . .
My analysis needs . . .

▶ **Revise** Now revise your literary analysis.

Grammar SUBJECT-VERB AGREEMENT

The **subject and verb** in a sentence must agree in number.

- A **singular verb** tells what one person, place, or thing is doing. It usually ends in *-s* or *-es*.
- A **plural verb** tells what more than one person, place, or thing is doing. It usually does not end in *-s* or *-es*.

Example

Singular Subject and Verb	Plural Subject and Verb
A **noise comes** from below.	The **noises come** from below.
Usher closes the door to the vault.	**We close** the door to the vault.

▶ **Put an *X* next to the sentences that have subject-verb agreement errors.**

1. The man enter a dimly lit room.   X
2. Usher suffers from an evil disease. _____
3. Usher and his sister looks very ill. _____
4. She disappear into the darkness. _____
5. They slide the casket into the empty vault. _____
6. The guest tremble with fear. _____

▶ **Rewrite the following sentences with correct subject-verb agreement. (Be sure to keep all the sentences in present tense.)**

7. A gust of wind throw Usher to the floor!

_____

8. The casket scrape against the stone floor.

_____

9. The walls of the house crumbles to the ground.

_____

10. Usher and his family disappears forever.

_____

▶ **Edit Your Draft.** Take a close look at each sentence in your draft. **Do the subjects and verbs agree?** Fix the ones that do not.

Mechanics USING POSSESSIVE NOUNS

A **possessive noun** shows ownership.

- Add an apostrophe (') and an -s to a singular noun.
- Add an apostrophe to a plural noun that ends in -s.

Example

Correct	Incorrect
Poe's story scared me.	Poes story scared me.
The friends' voices were low.	The friends voices were low.

▶ **Find and correct five errors in this paragraph.**

Student Model

CHECK AND CORRECT

❑ Correct one subject-verb agreement error.

❑ **UNDERLINE** two errors with possessives and correct them.

❑ **CIRCLE** two spelling errors and correct them.

   In Edgar Allan Poe's short story, "The Fall of the House of Usher," Madeline was the most innteresting character. She and her brother suffer from a terrible mentul illness. Madelines illness is more severe, though. She never speaks in the entire story. She simply walk around like a ghost. Then, readers learn that she and Usher are twins. In the end, the siblings death provide a hint about the destruction of the ancient House of Usher.

▶ **Edit Your Draft.** Look at the sentences in your draft. **Are all the possessive nouns correct?** Fix the ones that are not.

Final Draft/Present

▶ **Write a final draft of your literary analysis on the computer or on paper. Check it again and correct any errors before you present it.**

Focus Skill | Make Decisions

Read a Movie Review

Movie reviews help you decide what films to see. A movie review summarizes a film and gives the reviewer's opinion of it.

▶ **Read the movie review. Then answer the questions below.**

MARK IT

- **UNDERLINE** the title of the movie being reviewed.
- **CIRCLE** the genre of the movie.
- **★STAR** when the movie opens in theaters.

www.moviereviewmania.com

MOVIE REVIEW MANIA

The Best Fright of Your Life

by Marcel Jean

June 18, 2011

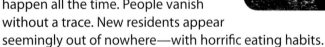

Imagine living in a world where night never ends. That's life for the residents of Nocturna. There, strange things happen all the time. People vanish without a trace. New residents appear seemingly out of nowhere—with horrific eating habits.

The film opens as a group of teenagers witness a mysterious shadow rising from the lake. Sensing danger, most of them don't stick around long enough to find out what it is. Except one boy. No one ever sees him again.

When *Eternal Night of Shadows* opens in theaters, it will be one of summer's biggest blockbusters. I went expecting to see a typical scary movie. But I was pleasantly surprised—and seriously frightened. Go see this movie! You will be afraid to leave your seat. You will be afraid to stay in your seat.

Eternal Night of Shadows

3-D, Horror, Fantasy

Rated PG-13

Starring Jeremy Joe, Tiffany Marker, and Vincent Pardilla as the Grand Elder

Distributed by Fear Factor Films

In theaters: July 4, 2011

❶ Who wrote this movie review?

Ⓐ Fear Factor Films

Ⓑ Marcel Jean

Ⓒ Jeremy Joe

Ⓓ Tiffany Marker

❷ What is the reviewer's opinion about the movie?

Ⓐ It will be a blockbuster hit.

Ⓑ It is like all other scary movies.

Ⓒ It will be a waste of time to see it.

Ⓓ It was a funny movie.

❸ Based on this review, would you go and see this film? Why or why not?

I would/would not (circle one) go and see this movie because _____

_____

_____

_____

_____

Special Effects Artist
Norman Cabrera

This monster maker has worked on *X-Men, Hulk,* and *Men in Black 3.*

▶ **Read the interview and job information. Then answer the questions below about Norman Cabrera's job.**

S **Scholastic: How did you get started making monsters?**

Norman Cabrera: I was always obsessed with old monster movies. I studied books on how to make masks and special effects. When I was 16, I saw the famous special-effects makeup artist Rick Baker on a TV show. I wrote him a fan letter and included a picture of my work. He called my house three weeks later! We stayed in touch. I also had supportive teachers.

S **How did you make it to Hollywood?**

The year after I graduated from high school, I worked on a low-budget horror movie in Florida, where I grew up. Then I called Rick Baker and told him I was ready for "the big time." He invited me to work an entry-level job for him.

S **When you're working, where do your ideas come from?**

The concept for a character comes from a screenwriter or director. They give me guidelines. Then, I start looking at books. I have nature books and anatomy books at my house. The design process takes a long time. I sketch and create models in clay before we decide on a final design.

① **What is one step Norman Cabrera took to start his career?**

_____

_____

② **How exciting do you think Cabrera's job is? Mark the line.**

👎 1 —— 2 —— 3 —— 4 —— 5 👍

Not very exciting   Very exciting

③ **I think Cabrera's job is/isn't** (circle one) **exciting because**

_____

_____

ON THE JOB

LOCATION
Los Angeles, California

EDUCATION
High school degree, on-the-job training

RESPONSIBILITIES
- Designs and creates masks
- Makes artificial body parts
- Follows directions from screenwriters and directors

SKILLS
- Creating horror character makeup with pencils, paints, clay, and computers
- Researching story characters

SALARY
Up to $100,000

ADVICE TO STUDENTS
"Believe in yourself. Get out there and make connections."

CAREER CONNECTION

Arts, A/V Technology, and Communication
www.careerclusters.org

Related Jobs
- scriptwriter
- movie director
- production assistant

Pitch your idea for a scary movie.

Your team has been hired by a movie director to set "The Fall of the House of Usher" in modern times. Write a proposal, or "pitch," about how to update the story.

❶ **Take notes.** Review page 149. Then, summarize the story elements below.

Element	Original Story
Setting	Place: Time:
Characters	
Plot Events	

❷ **Collaborate.** Brainstorm how this story could interest today's moviegoers.

Element	Update for the Movie Version
Setting	Place: Time:
Characters	
Special Effects/ Other Changes	

❸ **Pitch your ideas.** Select your best ideas from page 172 to complete the movie pitch below. Justify each change you propose.

MOVIE TITLE

_____

PRODUCTION TEAM: What is the name of your production team?

_____

SETTING: Where should the updated film be set?

We propose setting this movie _____

_____

because _____

_____

CHARACTERS & ACTORS: Which actors would you cast in the film?

• The character of Roderick Usher should be played by _____

because _____

_____

• The character of _____ should be played by _____

because _____

_____

• The character of _____ should be played by _____

because _____

_____

SPECIAL EFFECTS/OTHER CHANGES

_____

_____

_____

_____

Comprehension

▶ **Fill in the circle next to the correct answer.**

1. What is the main setting for "The Fall of the House of Usher"?
- Ⓐ Poe's house
- Ⓑ Madeline's backyard
- Ⓒ Usher's house
- Ⓓ the narrator's living room

2. Based on this story, you can tell that Madeline _____.
- Ⓐ is in love with the narrator
- Ⓑ has been sick for a long time
- Ⓒ loves her family's home
- Ⓓ doesn't get along with Usher

Here's a Tip.
Some questions ask for answers not directly stated in the text. Make sure text evidence supports your response.

3. What happens to Usher's house after the narrator leaves?
- Ⓐ It becomes haunted.
- Ⓑ It sinks into the water.
- Ⓒ It is sold.
- Ⓓ It is turned into a museum.

CRITICAL READING

4. Evaluate: Which adjectives best describe the narrator at the end of the story?
- Ⓐ happy and excited
- Ⓑ depressed and lonely
- Ⓒ unhappy and anxious
- Ⓓ anxious and terrified

CRITICAL READING

5. Synthesize: How are the story and the poem similar?
- Ⓐ Both are by Edgar Allan Poe.
- Ⓑ Both are set in modern times.
- Ⓒ Both have a dark and eerie mood.
- Ⓓ Both have main characters who help a friend.

Vocabulary

► **Fill in the circle next to the correct definition of the underlined word.**

1. Many <u>generations</u> of the Usher family had lived and died in this house.

   Ⓐ all the enemies   Ⓒ all the pets ever owned

   Ⓑ all the friends   Ⓓ all members of the same age

2. When Usher's sister died, he was filled with <u>despair</u>.

   Ⓐ hopefulness   Ⓒ great unhappiness

   Ⓑ lack of feeling   Ⓓ chills

3. "I hear the noises," Usher <u>uttered</u>.

   Ⓐ imagined   Ⓒ laughed

   Ⓑ wrote   Ⓓ said

► **Choose the correct synonym for the underlined word.**

4. Usher's house was very <u>peculiar</u>.

   Ⓐ dark   Ⓒ old

   Ⓑ strange   Ⓓ gloomy

► **Choose the correct word to complete the sentence.**

5. This story gave me a feeling of _____.

   Ⓐ anxiously   Ⓒ anxiety

   Ⓑ angry   Ⓓ anxious

Short Answer

CRITICAL READING

► **Synthesize:** Use what you've read in this Workshop to answer the question below. Check your spelling and grammar.

Why do you think Poe is known as the "Master of Horror"?

_____

_____

_____

_____

WORKSHOP 7

INFORMATIONAL TEXT

COMPREHENSION FOCUS
Cause and Effect

CRITICAL READING FOCUS
Analyze
Synthesize
Evaluate

Reading 1 Freaky Fish Invasion | **News Article**

Reading 2 Island of Snakes | **Magazine Article**

Reading 3 America's Least Wanted | **Science Text**

Alien INVADERS

Help! The aliens have invaded!

But these aliens don't come from outer space. They're plants and animals from other countries. When they land in the U.S., alien invaders cause huge problems. They destroy the environment. They kill native plants and animals. They even threaten people.

Scientists know these invaders must be stopped. The question is: How?

Academic Vocabulary

Target Word	Meaning	Example
● **Target Word** ▶ Read the Target Words. Rate each one using the scale below.*	**Meaning** ▶ Read the Target Word meanings. Write in the missing words.	**Example** ▶ Finish the Target Word examples below. Write in the missing ones.
invade (p. 178) in•vade (verb) ① ② ③ ④	to _____ into a place and cause _____	If killer bees came to **invade** my town, I would stay inside and lock all the doors and windows.
environment (p. 181) en•vi•ron•ment (noun) ① ② ③ ④	surroundings or habitat	• Some things I can do to help the **environment** include _____ _____ • _____
threaten (p. 182) threat•en (verb) ① ② ③ ④	to be likely to _____ something	• Pollution and wasting energy are two things that **threaten** _____ • _____
alter (p. 182) al•ter (verb) ① ② ③ ④	to _____ in some way	• If I could **alter** _____ I would _____ • _____
method (p. 187) meth•od (noun) ① ② ③ ④	a way of doing something	• The **method** I use to _____ is _____ • _____

Rating Scale
① = I don't know the word.   **③** = I think I know the word.
② = I've seen it or heard it.   **④** = I know it and use it.

The Key Idea

▶ **WRITE** What is this article mostly about?

_____

_____

VOCABULARY
Target Word

poisonous

poi•son•ous (adjective)

Rate It: ① ② ③ ④

Meaning

containing poison that is

_____

Example

_____

_____ that is

poisonous may cause serious

harm if it is swallowed.

React and Write

▶ **WRITE** Do you think it is right for scientists to kill invader species? Why or why not?

Summarize

In one or two sentences, summarize the problems that scientists have with snakehead fish. Include the topic and important details.

The Chinese snakehead fish is an invader species.

Freaky Fish Invasion

Scientists Stalk the Snakehead

September 4—Last week, top scientists rushed to a small pond in Maryland. The pond had been invaded by some very strange fish. And the fish were causing major problems!

The freaky fish were northern snakeheads from China. Snakehead fish are three feet long and slimy. Their skin is covered with black spots.

How did these alien invaders get here? They were brought into the U.S. illegally. Then someone dumped them into the Maryland pond.

Snakeheads have big mouths and sharp teeth. They are very powerful predators. So, the other fish didn't have a chance. The snakeheads ate them up.

The scientists had another thing to worry about. The Little Patuxent River is near the pond. Because snakeheads can crawl short distances across land, they might reach the river. They'd kill the fish there, too.

To stop the snakeheads, police sprayed **poisonous** chemicals into the water. As a result, the snakeheads died. Then scientists filled the pond with native fish. The pond is safe—until the next invader arrives. END

Words to Know! **native** originally from an area

Comprehension Focus
Cause and Effect

A **cause** is the reason something happens. An **effect** is the result of a cause. To find the cause and effect:

- Ask yourself "Why did it happen?" to find the cause.
- Ask yourself "What happened?" to find the effect.
- Look for signal words or phrases such as *because*, *so*, *as a result*, *therefore*, *consequently*, and *for this reason.*

▶ **Complete this chart with the cause-and-effect relationships in "Freaky Fish Invasion."**

Cause

_____
_____
_____
_____
_____
_____

Effect

So, the other fish got caught in their grip. The snakeheads ate them up.
_____
_____
_____
_____

Cause

_____
_____
_____
_____
_____
_____

Effect

_____
_____
_____
_____
_____
_____

The Key Idea

▶ **WRITE** What is this article mostly about?

_____

_____

VOCABULARY
Target Word

interfere

in•ter•fere (verb)

Rate It: ① ② ③ ④

Meaning

to get into or do things in a situation where you _____

_____

Example

Please do not **interfere** with me when _____

_____

React and Write

▶ **WRITE** What do you think Guam should do about the brown tree snake?

Island of SNAKES

Fifty years ago, the brown tree snake arrived in Guam. Life hasn't been the same since.

If you visit the island of Guam, watch out for snakes. They hang from the trees. They hide in the bushes. They might even slither into your bed while you're sleeping!

Snakes Take Over

Guam is a tiny island in the middle of the Pacific Ocean. Brown tree snakes arrived here from New Guinea, another island. Nobody meant to bring the snakes to Guam. They crawled onto military planes and ships by accident. Then they slithered off onto the island. When they did, everything changed.

Brown tree snakes are an alien species to the island. Because they have no natural predators on Guam, the snakes keep multiplying. In fact, they're completely out of control. Currently, there are more than 13,000 snakes per square mile on the island.

Words to Know!   **multiply**   to grow in number rapidly

Above, the brown tree snake hangs from a tree in Guam. At right, a woman holds a full-grown brown tree snake.

Dangerous Damage

Since invading Guam, the brown tree snakes have damaged the island's environment. They've killed and eaten native lizards, birds, and small mammals. As a result, 10 of the 12 species of birds are now extinct. The brown tree snakes ate them all!

The snakes **interfere** with life on Guam in other ways. They like to hang out on power lines. Because they weigh so much, the power lines snap. They have caused more than 1,600 power outages. For this reason, the lights go out regularly. Refrigerators break down. Computer screens go blank. It costs a lot to fix the damage caused by the snakes. ➤

Cause and Effect

1. ▶ **WRITE** In "Snakes Take Over," identify the cause for the fast spread of brown tree snakes.

_____

_____

_____

2. **UNDERLINE** Mark signal words and phrases in "Dangerous Damage."

3. ▶ **WRITE** "Dangerous Damage" mentions two effects of power outages. What are they?

• _____

_____

• _____

_____

CRITICAL READING
Synthesize

▶ **WRITE** What rules or laws could help to protect islands like Guam against invader species in the future?

_____

_____

_____

_____

_____

_____

Active Reading

CIRCLE What does a brown tree snake bite feel like?

VOCABULARY
 Target Word

release

re•lease (verb)

Rate It: ① ② ③ ④

Meaning

to _____

something

Example

A skunk **releases** a terrible

_____

when people get too close.

 React and Write

▶ **WRITE** Which animal is more harmful—the brown tree snake or the snakehead fish? Why?

 **Summarize**

In one or two sentences, summarize the topic and important details in "People vs. Snakes."

The snakes don't eat people, but they *do* bite.

Brown tree snakes are collected in Guam—and destroyed.

People vs. Snakes

The brown tree snakes also threaten people. They crawl into houses. They creep inside schools. What are they looking for? Food!

The snakes don't eat people, but they *do* bite. What happens when a brown tree snake bites you? You will be in pain, but you won't die. The venom is only mildly poisonous. The bite feels like a very bad bee sting.

The snakes are more dangerous for children. Children can't fight off a snake as well. Because the snake can get a better grip around a small victim, its bite **releases** more venom. The venom is so powerful that some children have trouble breathing after a brown tree snake bite.

Endless Battle

Brown tree snakes have altered Guam forever. Now, scientists fear the snakes might invade other islands, too. The same phenomenon that happened in Guam could happen in other countries. The snakes might become an international problem.

Some time ago, brown tree snakes were found at an airport in Hawaii. Scientists knew they had to stop the snakes before they caused a disaster. Therefore, they killed the snakes right away.

The battle with the brown tree snake goes on. In the end, everyone hopes that the scientists will win. **END**

Words to Know! **phenomenon** an event of scientific interest

Comprehension Focus

Cause and Effect

► Complete this chart with the cause-and-effect relationships in "People vs. Snakes" and "Endless Battle."

Cause

A brown tree snake bites you.
_____
_____
_____

Effect

_____
_____
_____
_____

Cause

_____
_____
_____
_____

Effect

_____
_____
_____
_____

Cause

_____
_____
_____
_____

Effect

_____
_____
_____
_____

READING 3

Science Text

💡 The Key Idea

▶ **WRITE** What is this science text mostly about?

_____

_____

◎ VOCABULARY Target Word

responsible

re•spon•si•ble (adjective)

Rate It: ① ② ③ ④

Meaning

being the _____

_____ something

Example

I am **responsible** for _____

_____

I am sorry!

❗ React and Write

▶ **WRITE** If someone planted a kudzu bush in a park near your home, what would you do?

184 WORKSHOP 7

AMERICA'S LEAST WANTED

KUDZU

RED FIRE ANTS

ZEBRA MUSSELS

NORTHERN SNAKEHEAD

Some animals and plants are bad for America. Find out the scary, gross facts about these alien invaders.

The Least-Wanted List

Did you know that the U.S. has a "Least-Wanted List"? It's true. But unlike the "Most-Wanted List," this isn't a list of people. It's a list of plants and animals. They have names like the Mexican fruit fly, the giant African snail, and the Asian long-horned beetle. Why are these creatures on the list? They're invader species.

Invader species are nonnative plants or animals that come from other countries. When they invade, they cause major damage. They can damage the environment, native plants and animals, and even the economy.

Attack of the Vines

One invader species is creeping all over the southern U.S. It's called kudzu. Kudzu is a vine brought here from Asia. At first, farmers used it to keep their land healthy. But soon, kudzu grew out of control. Because kudzu thrives in the warm climate of the South, it now covers eight million acres of land. It's not stopping, either. Kudzu can grow up to one foot a day. A single root can weigh 400 pounds!

Kudzu is **responsible** for destroying native forests. It climbs all over trees and blocks out the sunlight. As a result, the trees die. Kudzu can also wrap itself around a car. It can even blanket a house! People used to joke that kudzu might even creep into their windows at night and strangle them! Now kudzu is creeping into cities all over the U.S. ➤

| Words to Know! | **climate** | weather conditions |

Cause and Effect

1. **UNDERLINE** Mark three effects of invader species in "The Least-Wanted List."

2. ▶ **WRITE** In "Attack of the Vines," what caused kudzu to spread over eight million acres?

_____

_____

_____

REVIEW
Problem and Solution

1. **CIRCLE** What problem is discussed in "Attack of the Vines"?

2. ▶ **WRITE** How might people attempt to solve this problem?

_____

_____

_____

CRITICAL READING
Synthesize

▶ **WRITE** How could invader species harm the native plants and animals where you live?

_____

_____

_____

_____

_____

_____

Alien Invaders (185)

💡 Active Reading

★**STAR** What species is invading the food chain in the Great Lakes?

◎ VOCABULARY
Target Word

capable

ca•pa•ble (adjective)

Rate It: ① ② ③ ④

Meaning

_____ *to do something*

Example

A newborn baby is not capable of _____

_____

❗ React and Write

▶**WRITE** Most people don't know much about invader species. How should scientists get the word out?

💬 Summarize

▶**WRITE** Summarize the topic and important details in the science text "America's Least Wanted."

A Threat to the Food Chain

In the Great Lakes, one invader species is destroying nature's food chain. A food chain links different plants and animals together. Each species is food for the next one on the chain. If one plant or animal in the chain is destroyed, it affects the entire food chain.

Zebra mussels are harming the native food chain in the Great Lakes. The mussels came from Russia in 1988. They are eating the plankton in the lakes—food other fish depend on. So, the entire food chain is in danger.

A Deadly Sting

Some invader species are killers. In the 1930s, red fire ants arrived in the U.S. from South America. Before long, they were responsible for the deaths of thousands of animals. The ants attack an animal by crawling into its eyes and nose. Then they sting—all at once. The stings are deadly enough to kill a large animal like a deer.

 TEXT FEATURE Reading a Flowchart

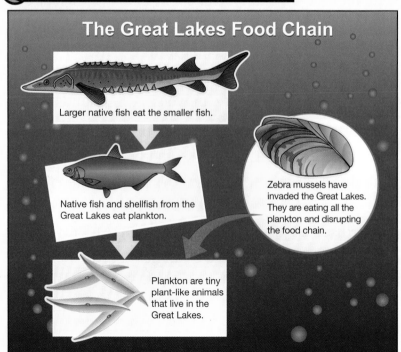

The Great Lakes Food Chain

Larger native fish eat the smaller fish.

Native fish and shellfish from the Great Lakes eat plankton.

Zebra mussels have invaded the Great Lakes. They are eating all the plankton and disrupting the food chain.

Plankton are tiny plant-like animals that live in the Great Lakes.

The U.S. government has methods for monitoring invasive species and stopping them. Field workers fight the invaders with poison, explosives, and electric shock. But we aren't **capable** of controlling every invader, because too many alien species are in too many places. So be on the lookout yourself—for America's Least Wanted! (END)

Words to Know!	**monitoring**	tracking or following

Red fire ants devour a baby bird.

A flowchart shows how the parts of a process are connected.

❶ Where are plankton on the food chain?

Ⓐ at the top Ⓑ at the bottom

Ⓒ in the middle Ⓓ they're not in the food chain

❷ What do large native fish typically eat?

_____

_____

❸ **Analyze:** How are zebra mussels disrupting the food chain?

_____

_____

Cause and Effect

1. (CIRCLE) Mark sentences in "A Deadly Sting" that describe the effects of an invader species.

2. ▶ WRITE What effects did this species have on deer and other animals in the U.S.?

_____

_____

_____

CRITICAL READING
Evaluate

▶ WRITE How serious is the problem of invader species? Mark the scale. Then explain your response using evidence from the reading.

```
•——————•——————•——————•——————•
1       2       3       4       5
not serious          extremely serious
```

_____

_____

_____

_____

_____

_____

Skills Check

1. ★STAR How are field workers fighting invader species?

2. ▶ WRITE Why can't we stop invader species?

_____

_____

WORD Challenge

◉ start

1 **Check them.** Which of these challenges are you **capable** of?

☐ running a mile in 10 minutes

☐ drawing a realistic picture of a friend

☐ dancing like someone from a music video

☐ making three shots in a row in basketball

2 Idioms An **idiom** is an expression that means something different from the separate words. An interesting idea can be called "food for thought." An easy task is "a piece of cake."

Match these idioms to their meanings.

"You'll knock their socks off!"   You might get into trouble.

"You're flirting with disaster!"   You'll impress them.

Now, finish these sentences:

I'll knock your socks off with my _____

_____

_____

I would be flirting with disaster if I _____

_____

_____

3 **Decide.** If you caught a **poisonous** bug, would you kill it, keep it as a pet, or **release** it outside?

I would _____

_____

because _____

_____

_____

4 **Describe it.** What would you **alter** in your neighborhood?

_____

_____

_____

_____

_____

_____

Some say this trick is hard, but for me, it's a **piece of cake!**

5 **Rate them.** Which of these people is most likely to **threaten** you? Rate them from **1** (*most* likely to **threaten**) to **4** (*least* likely to **threaten**).

☐ a newborn baby

☐ a neighborhood bully

☐ a kindergarten teacher

☐ a news reporter

8 Using a Dictionary

When you're not sure what a word means, look up the word in a dictionary. A dictionary will tell you the definition, or meaning, of the word.

Read the sentence, and write what you infer (guess) the underlined word means.

Cats and dogs belong to different animal species.

Inferred Meaning: _____

Now, look up the underlined word in the Glossary, and write the correct meaning.

Dictionary Meaning: _____

_____

How close was your guess? close/not close (circle one)

6

Choose it. Which **environment** would you most like to live in?

- ☐ a hot, humid one
- ☐ a cold, snowy one
- ☐ a wet, windy one
- ☐ a dry, dusty one

7

Check them. Which of these are you **responsible** enough to handle?

- ☐ babysitting a one-year-old
- ☐ being captain of a team
- ☐ cooking a meal for your family
- ☐ taking a celebrity on a tour of your school

9

Consider it. Which are the two worst things to do?

- ☐ **invading** a friend's email account
- ☐ **invading** a friend's privacy by listening in on his or her phone calls
- ☐ **invading** a friend's privacy by reading his or her journal
- ☐ **invading** a friend's privacy by going through his or her locker

10

Choose one. Your parents **interfere** in your social life. What is the best **method** for getting them to back off?

- ☐ Introduce them to your friends.
- ☐ Let them listen in on your phone calls.
- ☐ Tell them exactly where you are going and what time you'll be home.
- ☐ Other _____

⊙ finish

Writing Text Type
Argument Essay

An **argument essay** states a position or claim about an issue. The writer supports the claim with convincing evidence and reasons.

▶ **Read student Sam Roland's argument about a harmful invader species.**

Introduction

An **introductory statement** introduces the issue.

1. **UNDERLINE** the introductory statement.

A clear **thesis statement** presents the writer's claim about the issue.

2. **BOX** the thesis statement.

Body

Each body paragraph starts with a **topic sentence** that supports the writer's claim.

3. **UNDERLINE** the topic sentence in each paragraph.

Convincing reasons and relevant evidence support the argument.

4. ✔**CHECK** three reasons or pieces of evidence in the essay.

A strong argument points out weaknesses in **opposing arguments**.

5. →**PUT AN ARROW** next to one opposing argument.

Language Use

Transition words and phrases introduce or connect ideas.

6. CIRCLE five transitions.

Conclusion

The **conclusion** restates the thesis and offers a recommendation.

7. ★**STAR** the conclusion.

Student Model

Beware of Zebra Mussels!
by Sam Roland

All invader species damage the environment. However, I believe that zebra mussels are the most harmful invader species.

First of all, zebra mussels disrupt the food chain. In the Great Lakes, zebra mussels eat the plankton that small, native fish need to survive. Consequently, this hurts the native fish and the larger fish that feed on them.

Furthermore, zebra mussels could have a negative impact on human beings. Fishermen in the Great Lakes area may depend on the fish to make a living. When zebra mussels destroy the food chain, they may harm people's ability to earn a living.

Some people may claim that zebra mussels are not a widespread threat. They may argue that the species affects only a small area. However, a disruption of a food chain is a major threat to all the animals—and people—in the environment.

In summary, zebra mussels are responsible for a serious problem: a disruption of the food chain in the Great Lakes. Please write to your elected officials to demand that the government improve its methods for stopping this invader species.

Analyze the Text Type

▶ **Work with a partner to understand the purpose and form of an argument essay.**

Purpose: Argument Essay
The purpose of an argument essay is to _____ _____

Introduction

The **introductory paragraph** of an argument essay includes:
1. an _____ that introduces the issue.
2. a thesis statement that presents the _____ about the issue.

Student Model | In his introduction, Roland states:

1. the issue, which is: _____
2. his claim, which is: _____

Body

Body paragraphs provide **reasons and evidence** that support the writer's claim.
1. Each body paragraph starts with a _____
2. _____ support the topic sentence.
3. The writer points out weaknesses in the _____

Student Model

1. The topic sentence in the first body paragraph is: _____ _____

2. One piece of evidence that Roland includes in his first body paragraph is: _____

3. Roland addresses the opposing side's claim that _____ _____

Conclusion

The **conclusion** restates the _____ and offers a recommendation.

Student Model | Roland's recommendation is: _____ _____

Brainstorm

▶ Read the writing prompt. Then use the boxes to help you brainstorm ideas about the most harmful invader species.

Animal 1

Animal 2

Writing Prompt:
Write an argument essay about the most harmful invader species. Defend your argument with evidence from the Workshop readings.

Animal 3

Animal 4

State Your Position

▶ Select one of your ideas from the idea web. Then complete the sentences.

I will argue that _____

because _____

_____

Organize Ideas for Writing

▶ **Complete this outline with notes for your argument essay.**

I. Introduction List information about the issue you will argue.

    A. Issue: _____

    B. Claim: _____

    _____

II. Body Write a topic sentence for each body paragraph that supports your claim. Then list two reasons or pieces of evidence to support the topic sentence. Use one of your topic sentences to address an opposing argument.

    A. Topic Sentence 1: _____

    _____

        Evidence/Reason: _____

        Evidence/Reason: _____

    _____

    B. Topic Sentence 2: _____

    _____

        Evidence/Reason: _____

        Evidence/Reason: _____

    _____

    C. Topic Sentence 3: _____

    _____

        Evidence/Reason: _____

    _____

III. Conclusion Restate your thesis and make a recommendation.

    In summary, _____

    _____

    I suggest _____

    _____

Write Your Draft

▶ **Write a draft of your argument essay.**

Writing Prompt:
Write an argument essay about the most harmful invader species. Defend your argument with evidence from the Workshop readings.

| WORD CHOICES ||
Everyday	Precise
bother	provoke
keep	confine
stop	prohibit
home	habitat, environment

_____
(title of essay)

Introduction

▶ **Write your introductory statement.**

I believe that _____
(issue)

_____

▶ **Write your thesis statement.**

_____
(issue)

because _____

_____
(claim)

_____

▶ **Type your introduction on the computer or write it on paper. Then use these transition words and phrases to complete a draft of your argument essay.**

Body

One reason is that . . .	Another reason . . .
First of all, . . .	Most importantly, . . .
The worst thing . . .	Finally, . . .
In addition, . . .	Some people might argue that . . .

Conclusion

For these reasons, . . .	I recommend that . . .
In conclusion, . . .	It is important that . . .

Revise Your Argument Essay

▶ **Evaluate:** Rate your argument essay. Then have a partner rate it.

Scoring Guide			
needs improvement	average	good	excellent
1	**2**	**3**	**4**

1. **UNDERLINE** the introductory statement. Does it introduce the issue effectively?

   Self   1   2   3   4
   Partner   1   2   3   4

2. BOX the thesis statement. Does it present a claim effectively?

   Self   1   2   3   4
   Partner   1   2   3   4

3. **UNDERLINE** the topic sentence in each body paragraph. Does each one support the claim?

   Self   1   2   3   4
   Partner   1   2   3   4

4. ✔**CHECK** reasons and evidence. Are they convincing and relevant?

   Self   1   2   3   4
   Partner   1   2   3   4

5. →**PUT AN ARROW** next to an opposing argument. Does the essay point out a weakness?

   Self   1   2   3   4
   Partner   1   2   3   4

6. CIRCLE transition words and phrases. Do they connect ideas?

   Self   1   2   3   4
   Partner   1   2   3   4

7. ★**STAR** the conclusion. Does it offer a recommendation?

   Self   1   2   3   4
   Partner   1   2   3   4

▶ **Discuss:** Give feedback on your partner's argument essay.

1. Start with positive comments about your partner's argument essay.

   A strong part of your argument is _____
   _____

   The evidence I find most convincing is
   _____
   _____

2. Give your partner suggestions for revision.

   I have a question about _____
   _____

   Your argument would be stronger if ____
   _____
   _____

   Your essay needs to include _____
   _____

3. Answer any questions your partner has about your suggestions.

4. Ask your partner for feedback. Use the frames below to summarize your partner's feedback.

   A strong part of my argument was . . .
   You had a question about . . .
   My argument would be stronger if I . . .
   My essay needs . . .

▶ **Revise** Now revise your argument essay.

Grammar USING SUBJECT AND OBJECT PRONOUNS

A **pronoun** is a word that takes the place of a noun in a sentence.

- Use a **subject pronoun** in the subject of a sentence.
- Use an **object pronoun** after a verb or after a word such as *for* or *to*.

Example

Subject Pronoun	Object Pronoun
I never liked snakes.	Snakes have always scared **me**.
We want to leave the island.	Snakes are too gross for **us**.
She found two in the house.	One snake almost bit **her**.
They are just creepy.	My sister and I hate **them**.

► Circle the correct pronoun. Write whether it is a **subject** or **object** pronoun.

1. The snakehead fish tried to bite [he / him].   *object*

2. [He / Him] showed the fish to his parents.   _____

3. [They / Them] called the game warden.   _____

4. The game warden took the fish away with [her / she].   _____

5. Roberto has a photo of all of [them / they] with the fish.   _____

6. [I / Me] don't want to catch a snakehead fish.   _____

► Rewrite these sentences using a pronoun for the underlined words.

7. My grandmother said that ants have taken over her yard.

_____

8. She sprayed her rose garden to stop the invader ants.

_____

9. My sister helped Grandma cut down the kudzu.

_____

10. My cousins helped out in the yard, too.

_____

► **Edit Your Draft.** Take a close look at the sentences in your draft. **Do they use subject and object pronouns correctly?** Fix the ones that do not.

Usage AVOIDING DOUBLE NEGATIVES

Negatives are words that express *no* or *not*.

- Use only one negative word to express a single negative idea.
- It is incorrect to use two negatives to express a negative idea.

Example

Correct	Incorrect
Kudzu should never be allowed to grow near homes and schools.	Kudzu shouldn't never be allowed to grow near homes and schools.
The brown tree snake didn't bite anyone.	The brown tree snake didn't bite nobody.

▶ **Find and correct five errors in this paragraph.**

Student Model

> Us believe that kudzu is the worst invader species. One reason is that this plant grows outta control. It is capeable of growing twelve inches a day. Another reason why kudzu is dangerous is that it destroys native plant species. Kudzu won't let no other plant grow. The government shouldn't never let people grow kudzu plants in their backyards.

CHECK AND CORRECT

- ☐ Correct two double-negative errors.
- ☐ **UNDERLINE** one subject-object pronoun error and correct it.
- ☐ CIRCLE two spelling errors and correct them.

▶ **Edit Your Draft.** Look at the sentences in your own draft. **Do they use double negatives?** Fix the ones that do.

Final Draft/Present

▶ **Write a final draft of your essay on the computer or on paper. Check it again and correct any errors before you present it.**

Focus Skill | Solve Problems

Read a Public Notice

A public notice shares information about a change, or warns people about a possible threat in the environment.

▶ **Read the public notice about an invasive plant species. Then answer questions below.**

MARK IT

- **UNDERLINE** the subject of the public notice.

- CIRCLE the name of the group that created the notice.

- ★**STAR** the creator's contact information.

PUBLIC NOTICE

Members of the public are hereby prohibited from collecting the Giant Hogweed plant from this area. Violation of this notice will result in a fine of $500, in accordance with Public Law 112–21c.

About the Giant Hogweed:

- Common names: giant hogweed, cartwheel flower
- Scientific name: *Heracleum mantegazzianum*
- native to Europe and Asia, introduced in U.S. in 1917
- highly invasive plant that crowds out native species
- produces toxic sap that causes skin irritation and blindness

For more information, visit the Center for Invasive Species and Ecosystem Health at www.invasive.org.

---

1 **What does the notice warn the public about?**

Ⓐ that invasive species grow in the area

Ⓑ that people should not collect giant hogweed plants

Ⓒ that people should not litter in the area

Ⓓ that people should not walk in the area

2 **The public notice is likely NOT targeted at which of the following people?**

Ⓐ a government official

Ⓑ a family going on a nature walk

Ⓒ a plant biologist

Ⓓ a group of students and teachers on a field trip

3 **Is the public notice an effective way to solve the problem in this environment? Why or why not?**

_____

_____

_____

_____

_____

_____

_____

_____

_____

Botanist
Mauricio Diazgranados

Meet a botanist who climbs mountains to study endangered plants.

▶ **Read the schedule and job information. Then answer the questions below about Mauricio Diazgranados's job.**

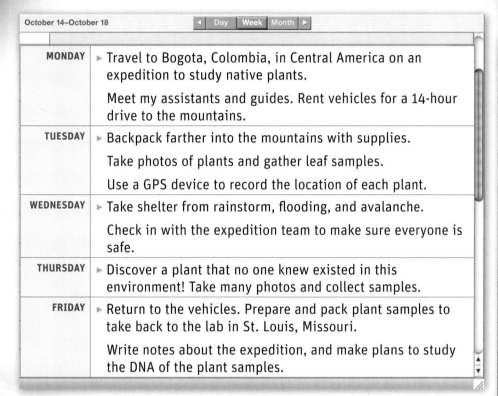

October 14–October 18	◀ Day **Week** Month ▶
MONDAY	▶ Travel to Bogota, Colombia, in Central America on an expedition to study native plants. Meet my assistants and guides. Rent vehicles for a 14-hour drive to the mountains.
TUESDAY	▶ Backpack farther into the mountains with supplies. Take photos of plants and gather leaf samples. Use a GPS device to record the location of each plant.
WEDNESDAY	▶ Take shelter from rainstorm, flooding, and avalanche. Check in with the expedition team to make sure everyone is safe.
THURSDAY	▶ Discover a plant that no one knew existed in this environment! Take many photos and collect samples.
FRIDAY	▶ Return to the vehicles. Prepare and pack plant samples to take back to the lab in St. Louis, Missouri. Write notes about the expedition, and make plans to study the DNA of the plant samples.

1 What risks does Mauricio Diazgranados take to study endangered plant species?

_____

_____

_____

2 How exciting do you think Diazgranados's job is? Mark the line.

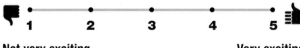

1   2   3   4   5

Not very exciting   **Very exciting**

3 I think Diazgranados's job is/isn't (circle one) exciting because _____

_____

ON THE JOB

LOCATION
St. Louis, Missouri

EDUCATION
Bachelor's degree; Master's degree in Biology

RESPONSIBILITIES
- Studies and collects plants
- Works in a lab to study the DNA of plants

SKILLS
- Researching and organizing information
- Leading and managing an expedition team

SALARY
$60,000–$70,000

FAVORITE PART OF WORK
"I enjoy seeing landscapes, lakes, and waterfalls while doing work that I love."

CAREER CONNECTION

Agriculture, Food, and Natural Resources
www.careerclusters.org

Related Jobs
- lab assistant
- ecotourism guide
- science teacher

Create a public notice.

Invader plant and animal species threaten the environment. Create a public notice warning people about an invader species that poses the greatest public threat.

❶ **Collaborate.** Review the Workshop readings. Decide as a team on three invader species that pose a serious public threat.

- ❏ the snakehead fish
- ❏ the red fire ant
- ❏ kudzu
- ❏ the brown tree snake
- ❏ the zebra mussel
- ❏ plankton

❷ **Evaluate evidence.** From the list above, select one species that poses the greatest public threat. Justify your selection.

We believe that _____ species poses the

greatest public threat because _____

_____

_____

_____

_____

❸ **Take notes.** Write details about the invader species you selected above.

Information about _____

- • _____

   _____

- • _____

   _____

- • _____

   _____

- • _____

   _____

④ **Prepare and present the public notice.** Include an image to go with the information.

PUBLIC NOTICE

CAPTION/LABEL: _____

_____

_____

MESSAGE: _____

_____

_____

_____

ABOUT THE _____

- _____
- _____
- _____
- _____

FOR MORE INFORMATION, _____

_____

_____

THIS PUBLIC NOTICE WAS CREATED BY _____

VISIT OR CONTACT US AT _____

Comprehension

▶ **Fill in the circle next to the correct answer.**

1. What causes northern snakeheads to eat other fish?
- Ⓐ They do not want to share their habitat with other animals.
- Ⓑ They are treated very badly by other kinds of fish.
- Ⓒ They have big mouths and sharp teeth.
- Ⓓ They are predators who eat other fish to survive.

CRITICAL READING

2. Synthesize: What is the best way for countries to prevent alien animal species from causing destruction?
- Ⓐ They can kill off all their snake populations.
- Ⓑ They can check all arriving planes and ships for snakes.
- Ⓒ They can warn their citizens to stay away from Guam.
- Ⓓ They can tell people not to eat zebra mussels.

3. Which is an effect of invader species?
- Ⓐ They build and strengthen food chains.
- Ⓑ They kill native plants and animals.
- Ⓒ They return to their native environment.
- Ⓓ All of the above.

4. What effects does kudzu have when it invades?
- Ⓐ It creeps into homes and strangles people as they sleep.
- Ⓑ It causes air pollution and hurts the economy.
- Ⓒ It buries cars and houses, and destroys native plants.
- Ⓓ It makes soil healthier and helps native plants grow.

CRITICAL READING

5. Analyze: What can happen when an invader species interrupts a food chain?
- Ⓐ The invader eats food sources that other species need.
- Ⓑ The invaders are killed immediately.
- Ⓒ There's still plenty of food for every species to eat.
- Ⓓ The climate can change.

> **Here's a Tip.**
> Look for words like *cause, effect, problem,* and *solution* in questions. These cue words can help you figure out what kind of answer is expected.

Vocabulary

▶ **Fill in the circle next to the correct definitions of the underlined words.**

1. Brown tree snakes have <u>altered</u> the <u>environment</u>.

   Ⓐ left, city   Ⓒ changed, habitat
   Ⓑ infested, country   Ⓓ taken over, homes

2. The snakehead fish <u>invaded</u> a pond in Maryland.

   Ⓐ moved into and harmed   Ⓒ cleaned
   Ⓑ moved out of before harming Ⓓ ate

3. One <u>method</u> scientists use to kill invader species is poisoning them.

   Ⓐ trick   Ⓒ way of doing something
   Ⓑ payment of money   Ⓓ drug

▶ **Fill in the circle next to the best answer.**

4. To be "in hot water" means to be in trouble. Which sentence uses this idiom correctly?

   Ⓐ When Tamyra touched the boiling tea, she was in hot water.
   Ⓑ Lia was in hot water with her parents after coming home past curfew.
   Ⓒ Miguel enjoyed taking a bath in hot water.
   Ⓓ To make broth, sprinkle this powder into hot water.

▶ **Look up the underlined word in the Glossary. Choose the best definition.**

5. Travelers <u>persist</u> in bringing new animals and plants to our country illegally.

   Ⓐ to continue doing something Ⓒ to resist doing something
   Ⓑ to enjoy doing something   Ⓓ to stop doing something

Short Answer

CRITICAL READING

▶ **Evaluate: Use what you've read in this Workshop to answer the question below. Check your spelling and grammar.**

Which invader species do you think is worst for the U.S.? Why?

_____

_____

_____

WORKSHOP 8

INFORMATIONAL TEXT

COMPREHENSION FOCUS
Compare and Contrast

CRITICAL READING FOCUS
Analyze
Synthesize
Evaluate

Turning Points

What does it mean to be "at a turning point"? It means getting ready for something totally new and different. Often, when teens make the transition into adulthood, they find themselves at a turning point.

Get ready to meet some impressive teens who have experienced a turning point—and triumphed. They have overcome tough challenges and turned their lives around.

Academic Vocabulary

Target Word ▶ Read the Target Words. Rate each one using the scale below.*	Meaning ▶ Read the Target Word meanings. Write in the missing words.	Example ▶ Finish the Target Word examples below. Write in the missing ones.
positive (p. 206) *pos•i•tive* (adjective) ① ② ③ ④	very _____ that something is _____	• I'm *positive* that I will _____ _____ this year. • _____ _____
involved (p. 209) *in•volved* (adjective) ① ② ③ ④	included in a group, activity, or event	• If you get *involved* in _____ _____ , you will _____ _____ • _____ _____
dramatic (p. 210) *dra•ma•tic* (adjective) ① ② ③ ④	very large and _____	• _____ would make a *dramatic* change in my life. • _____ _____
attitude (p. 213) *at•ti•tude* (noun) ① ② ③ ④	an opinion or feeling about something	• _____ helped me to develop a good *attitude* about _____ • _____ _____
persist (p. 215) *per•sist* (verb) ① ② ③ ④	to _____ doing something even if it is _____	 I will **persist** in finishing this race even though I'm extremely tired.

***Rating Scale** ① = I don't know the word. ③ = I think I know the word.
② = I've seen it or heard it. ④ = I know it and use it.

Turning Points 205

Personal Essay

The Key Idea

▶ **WRITE** What is this personal essay mostly about?

_____

_____

VOCABULARY
Target Word

purpose

pur•pose (noun)

Rate It: ① ② ③ ④

Meaning

a _____

for doing something

Example

My **purpose** for _____

_____ is to

_____

_____

React and Write

▶ **WRITE** Jonathan was given a label at school, and he didn't like it. Do students at your school label each other? Is that fair?

Summarize

In one or two sentences, summarize the problems Jonathan had when he moved to the United States. Include the topic and important details.

Starting Over

Moving to the U.S. Changed Everything

by Jonathan Fong

I used to be one of the coolest guys in my school, but that was in Taiwan. In the U.S., classmates called me boring. Moving to the U.S. meant starting over.

I grew up in Taiwan, a small island near China. Then, four years ago, my mother sent me here for the **purpose** of getting a better education.

Jonathan Fong moved to the U.S. in high school.

I worked hard at school in both Taiwan and the U.S. In Taiwan, my hard work paid off with good grades. However, in the U.S., school was a struggle because I didn't understand English. My grades suffered.

Finding new friends was even more difficult. I had always been outgoing and friendly. In Taiwan, I had a lot of friends and went out all the time.

In the U.S., I was still outgoing and I tried to make friends, but people didn't accept me. My new classmates thought I was totally uncool. Some people harassed me. They even gave me a label— the "boring foreign kid who doesn't speak English."

I didn't let the label get me down. I knew that once I learned English, I'd be able to make friends. After a year in the U.S., my life has improved a lot. I have friends, and I am positive that I want to go to college in the U.S. Best of all, I no longer have a negative label. **END**

Words to Know! **harassed** picked on or made fun of

Comprehension Focus

Compare and Contrast

When you **compare**, you tell how two people or things are alike. When you **contrast**, you tell how they are different. To compare and contrast:

- Ask yourself how two things are the same. Look for signal words such as *both*, *too*, *also*, and *in addition*.

- Ask yourself how two things are different. Look for signal words such as *but*, *rather than*, and *however*.

▶ Complete this chart to compare and contrast Jonathan's life in Taiwan and his life in the U.S. in "Starting Over."

Jonathan in Taiwan

Different

1. *Jonathan was the cool, popular one.*

2. _____

3. _____

Same

1. _____

2. _____

3. _____

Jonathan in the U.S.

Different

1. *Kids thought that Jonathan was boring.*

2. _____

3. _____

💡 The Key Idea

▶ **WRITE** What is this profile mostly about?

_____

_____

_____

◎ Target Word

initiate

i•ni•ti•ate (verb)

Rate It: ① ② ③ ④

Meaning

to _____ something

Example

_I'll **initiate** a conversation with my friends about _____

_____

_____

❗ React and Write

▶ **WRITE** Ekiwah was dependent on others for many things. Why might being dependent be harder for a teen than for a young child?

WORDS Set

This teen grew up unable to walk. He had a choice—to give up, or to find a life that was uniquely his own.

Ekiwah Adler-Belendez is the author of several books of poetry. Here, he sits at home with his father.

Him Free

Poetry can change lives. Ekiwah (Eh-KEE-wah) Adler-Belendez is living proof. Ekiwah was born with several serious diseases. He needed to use a wheelchair to get around. But when this young man discovered poetry, his life changed forever.

A Big Challenge

Ekiwah was born in a rural Mexican village. At birth, doctors said that he had cerebral palsy and paralytic scoliosis. These diseases bent his back and made his legs weak. They made him dependent on others—for everything.

When Ekiwah was little, kids his age played outside. Unlike his friends, Ekiwah had to stay inside. He couldn't walk without braces. He required help to perform simple tasks like walking down stairs. "I couldn't just go climb a tree," says Ekiwah.

As the years went by, Ekiwah felt like he was missing out on his youth. He didn't feel involved in the fun other kids were having. Finding happiness was a challenge.

Discovering Poetry

Ever since he was little, Ekiwah's parents read poetry to him. By the time he turned 10, Ekiwah was writing poetry himself. He was able to express his ideas and feelings. He discovered a talent that was all his own.

At age 12, Ekiwah published a book of poetry. At 14, he produced a second book. Two years later, his third book came out. Many people admired Ekiwah's unique voice. Suddenly, he felt connected to the world rather than isolated from it. He even **initiated** new friendships. ➤

Words to Know!	**dependent**	needing help

 Compare and Contrast

1. **CIRCLE** Identify a paragraph that describes how Ekiwah was different from his friends when he was little.

2. ▶ **WRITE** How was Ekiwah's life different after he published books of poetry? Give two examples.

   • _____
   _____
   _____

   • _____
   _____
   _____

CRITICAL READING
Evaluate

▶ **WRITE** Which has had a bigger effect on Ekiwah: having illnesses, or becoming a poet? Give evidence from the text to support your response.

_____
_____
_____
_____
_____
_____

Active Reading

★STAR Why did Ekiwah need surgery?

VOCABULARY
Target Word

bond

bond (noun)

Rate It: ① ② ③ ④

Meaning

a feeling of _____

_____ people or groups

Example

My friends and I share a
bond because we all _____

_____

_____

React and Write

▶ **WRITE** What do you think has been the most important turning point in Ekiwah's life so far?

Summarize

In one or two sentences, summarize the topic and important details in "Road to Recovery."

Still Suffering

By age 15, Ekiwah had become famous as a poet. But he was still suffering because of his curved spine. Doctors said that if it curved any more, it would affect Ekiwah's speech and breathing. They recommended immediate surgery.

Ekiwah's parents tried to find help. They sent Ekiwah's X-rays to Dr. Roy Nuzzo, a top surgeon in New York City. They also sent Ekiwah's poetry. Because Dr. Nuzzo was a poet, too, he felt a **bond** with Ekiwah. He offered to operate for free.

Road to Recovery

The operation took 10 hours. Doctors inserted rods, screws, and wires to alter Ekiwah's spine.

Now, Ekiwah's back is stronger, and he can get around with a walker. Doctors are positive that Ekiwah is on the road to recovery.

Today, Ekiwah's life is very different than it was when he grew up. Rather than being dependent on others, Ekiwah can get around by himself. His home is still in Mexico. But now he travels around the world. While he remains close to his family, Ekiwah also has many friends and admirers.

Poetry has made a dramatic difference in Ekiwah's life. Words have truly set him free. ⟨END⟩

From the poem "Nothing" (abridged)
by Ekiwah Adler-Belendez

I feel like a tree that has no branches,
Like a warrior that has failed his mission,
Locked in a room with no door, no way out.
The earth like empty streets
No birds singing, only cars rushing by.
I feel like nothing.

The worst of thieves has robbed my smiles,
I know Nothing, and Nothing knows me.

Words to Know! | **surgeon** a doctor who performs operations

Comprehension Focus

Compare and Contrast

▶ Complete this chart to compare and contrast Ekiwah's life before and after he began writing poetry.

Ekiwah's Life Before

Different

1. Ekiwah's illnesses prevented him from moving around and being involved with others.

2. _____

_____

_____

3. _____

_____

_____

Same

1. _____

_____

_____

2. _____

_____

_____

3. _____

_____

_____

Ekiwah's Life After

Different

1. _____

_____

_____

2. _____

_____

_____

3. _____

_____

_____

☼ The Key Idea

▶ **WRITE** What is this life skills feature mostly about?

_____

_____

◎ VOCABULARY
Target Word

option

op•tion (noun)

Rate It: ① ② ③ ④

Meaning

a _____

_____

Example

_____

_____

would be my best **option** _for a summer job this year._

⊙ React and Write

▶ **WRITE** Waila and Dali each reacted differently to their mom's arrest. How would you react? More like Waila or more like Dali? Explain.

HARD

Two girls' lives were torn apart when their mom was put in prison. Only together could they build a new life.

An Empty Home

In 1999, sisters Waila, 15, and Dali, 12, immigrated to New York from the Dominican Republic with their mom. They were poor. They didn't have many friends. And they didn't speak English. Their mom was under a lot of pressure to make ends meet. Her only **option** was to work 12 hours a day. Waila and Dali learned to take care of themselves.

One day, the sisters came home after school and waited for their mom. But she never came home. Later, they learned that she had been arrested and would have to serve a jail sentence.

Waila and Dali felt like their mom had abandoned them. They were confused and sad, but they were also angry.

Family friends helped take care of the girls. But sometimes, they had to fend for themselves. Their mom missed many holidays and birthdays. She also missed several important events, like Waila's high school graduation and Dali's eighth grade graduation.

Different Reactions

Even though Waila and Dali faced the same circumstances, they reacted differently to their mom's

TIME

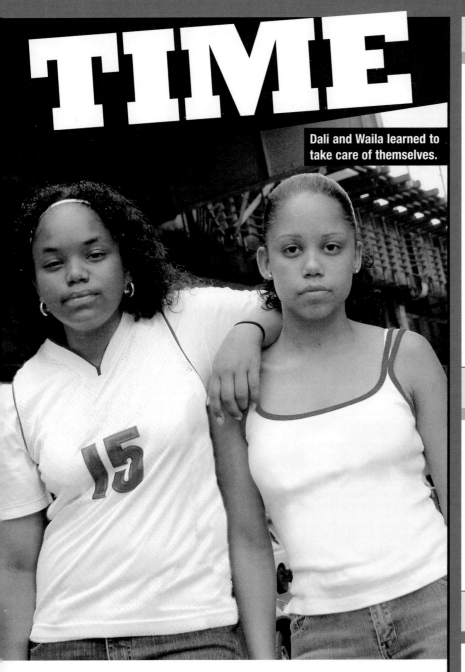

Dali and Waila learned to take care of themselves.

imprisonment. Waila didn't want anyone to know. She was embarrassed. She only told her closest friends.

Dali, however, had a different attitude. She didn't care what other people thought. If people said bad things about her mom, Dali ignored them. She didn't want anyone to pity them. "Nobody needs to feel sorry for us," she said. "We're doing fine."

The sisters were coping and surviving, each in her own way. ➤

Words to Know!	**pity**	to feel sorry for someone

Compare and Contrast

1. ▶ **WRITE** What feelings did the two sisters share about their mom's imprisonment?

_____

_____

_____

_____

2. CIRCLE Mark sentences that describe how the sisters reacted differently to their mom's imprisonment.

REVIEW
Cause and Effect

▶ **WRITE** What caused Waila and Dali's mom to miss their graduations?

_____

_____

_____

CRITICAL READING
Analyze

▶ **WRITE** How did the sisters' home life change after their mother went to jail?

_____

_____

_____

_____

_____

Active Reading

★**STAR** How many kids have a parent in prison?

VOCABULARY
Target Word

approximately

ap•prox•i•mate•ly *(adverb)*

Rate It: ① ② ③ ④

Meaning

figured out by guess or
_____,
but nearly _____

Example

There are **approximately**

_____
_____

in my neighborhood.

React and Write

▶ **WRITE** What would be the hardest thing about having a parent in jail?

Summarize

▶ **WRITE** Summarize the topic and important details and ideas in the life skills feature "Hard Time."

A National Problem

There are kids like Waila and Dali all over the United States. Recent statistics show that more than 2 million kids have a parent in prison.

Most of these children have an incarcerated father. But the number of children with an incarcerated mother is soaring. From 1991 to 2007, the number of mothers in jail jumped 131 percent. Today, **approximately** 1 out of every 50 kids has a parent in prison. Like Waila and Dali, they have to struggle to put their lives back together.

A Fresh Start

Before their mother went to jail, Waila and Dali weren't that close to her. But after she went to jail, their mother really tried to be a better parent. She involved her daughters in a program called Hour Children. The program sets up visits between children and parents in jail. It provides activities and support to help children and teens with incarcerated parents.

TEXT FEATURE Reading a Line Graph

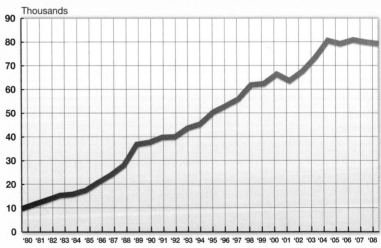

Annual Prison Admissions for Women

Source: Bureau of Justice, National Prisoner Statistics, 2009

The program helped both girls. Dali was able to express how hurt she was, having her mom in jail. She even started to write poetry. Waila's attitude was similar to her sister's. "I learned I could be myself," says Waila. "Being in the program made things a lot easier."

Finally, their mother was released from jail. But soon after, she was deported to the Dominican Republic. Since then, the sisters persisted in keeping their lives on the right track. Waila attended college. Dali made her high school honor society.

The two sisters made it past a tough turning point in their lives. They're excited about the future. And they're both positive about one thing—they don't have to make the mistakes their mom made. END

| Words to Know! | **deported**   sent back to country of origin |

Waila and Dali visit their mom in jail.

A line graph shows how information changes over time.

❶ Analyze: Which statement is true about women and prison in the U.S.?

Ⓐ Fewer women are in prison than ever before.

Ⓑ Far more women were in prison in 2009 than in 1980.

Ⓒ Women who are mothers spend less time in jail.

Ⓓ More women than men go to jail each year.

❷ When was the sharpest increase of women in prison?

Ⓐ 1989–1993   Ⓑ 2000–2001

Ⓒ 2002–2004   Ⓓ 2005–2008

❸ About how many more women were in prison in 1998 than in 1988?

Compare and Contrast

1. CIRCLE What was Waila and Dali's relationship with their mom like before she went to prison?

2. ▶ WRITE How did their mom change after she went to prison?

_____

_____

_____

CRITICAL READING

Synthesize

▶ WRITE How important is it for teenagers to have strong role models? Can teens learn from the mistakes their parents make?

_____

_____

_____

_____

_____

_____

_____

Skills Check

1. UNDERLINE How did Hour Children change Waila and Dali?

2. ▶ WRITE How are Waila and Dali different from their mom?

_____

_____

WORD Challenge

START

1 **Think about it.** What is one mistake you are **positive** you'll never make?

_____

_____

_____

_____

_____

2 ## Context Clues

Sometimes, you'll see an unfamiliar word in a sentence. One way to figure out what it means is to look at the words around it. The other words in the sentence or paragraph can provide context that helps you to determine the new word's meaning.

What do you think *excel* means? Study the context, and make a guess. Then check the Glossary to see if you got it right.

☐ to do poorly at something

☐ to enjoy something

☐ to do something very well

☐ to quit doing something

I **persisted** at running. Now, I **excel** at it!

3 **Identify it.** Which could be described as a **dramatic** announcement from a good friend?

☐ "I am bored."

☐ "I am moving to another country—tomorrow!"

☐ "I love that shirt!"

☐ "I had yogurt and granola for breakfast."

4 **Evaluate.** Your friend just lost another sports game. What do you say to help your friend keep a good **attitude**?

_____

_____

_____

5 Think about it.

Approximately how long would you **persist** at working on:

a hard video game? _____

a 500-piece puzzle? _____

trying to unlock a jammed locker? _____

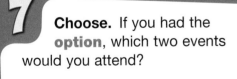

6 Name them.
List three people (or pets!) you have a strong **bond** with.

1. _____

2. _____

3. _____

7 Choose.
If you had the **option**, which two events would you attend?

____ a World Series championship

____ your favorite music awards

____ a Hollywood movie premiere

____ the opening of a new water park

8 Noun Endings ❷

To show more than one person, place, or thing, add an -s to most nouns.

If a noun ends in *ss*, *s*, *x*, *ch*, or *sh*, add *-es* to make it plural, as in *buses* and *dresses*.

If a noun ends in a consonant and *y*, change the *y* to *i* and add *-es* to make it plural, as in *spies*.

Watch out for irregular plurals like *mice*, the plural of *mouse*. These don't follow the rules!

Write the plural of each word below.

Singular	Plural
coach	_____
purpose	_____
child	_____
penny	_____
foot	_____

> I've got a winning **attitude**. The people on the other team have losing **attitudes**!

9 Identify it.
If you could **initiate** a whole-school discussion on one important topic, what would that topic be?

_____

_____

10 Check them.
How much would you like to be **involved** in each of these activities?

	not at all	depends	very much
a deep-sea diving trip	_____	_____	_____
a dance marathon	_____	_____	_____
a wilderness race	_____	_____	_____
a reality show on TV	_____	_____	_____

FINISH

Writing Text Type
Personal Narrative

A **personal narrative** tells a story about an experience in the writer's life.

▶ **Read Jay Theon's personal narrative about a turning point in his life.**

Introduction

The **introductory statement** identifies the topic of the personal narrative and engages the reader by establishing a point of view.

1. <u>UNDERLINE</u> the introductory statement.

Body

Body paragraphs describe events in **time order**.

2. **NUMBER** events 1–4 in time order.

Carefully chosen **sensory details** bring the story to life.

3. ✔**CHECK** four sensory details.

Dialogue shows exactly what people in the story said.

4. BOX two lines of dialogue.

Language Use

Transition words and phrases connect ideas and details.

5. CIRCLE five transition words or phrases.

Vivid adjectives describe the experience in a lively way.

6. <u>DOUBLE UNDERLINE</u> three vivid adjectives.

Conclusion

The **conclusion** sums up the experience and why it is important.

7. ★STAR the conclusion.

Student Model

Life as the New Kid
by Jay Theon

Last summer, my family moved to a new town and I started at a new school. I had been popular at my former school, but being a new kid quickly taught me how it feels to be an outsider.

The first day at school was awful. I didn't know where anything was. On the way to math class, I got lost and arrived late. Someone behind me whispered an insult as I sat down. "Mind your business," I hissed. The teacher marched over. "Theon," she said, "first you're late, and now you're interrupting?" My face burned with total embarrassment.

At lunch, I had no one to sit with. I felt lost in the overwhelming sea of students, and everyone stared at me as I ate my cardboard sandwich, all alone.

I thought about times when I had been nasty to a new kid. Once at my old school, a new boy had said hi, and I just ignored him. Another time, I laughed when a new girl walked into the wrong room. I wished I could go back in time and be supportive.

Eventually, I made friends, but that didn't erase the pain of that first day. Moving to a new town taught me what it's like to be the new kid. Now wiser, I always try to welcome new students.

Analyze the Text Type

▶ **Work with a partner to understand the purpose and form of a personal narrative.**

Purpose: Personal Narrative
The purpose of a personal narrative is to _____ _____

Introduction

The **introductory statement** of a personal narrative identifies _____
_____

Student Model | In his introduction, Jay Theon identifies the topic, which is: _____

_____

_____

Body

The **body paragraphs** describe the story's events, experiences, and setting.

1. Events are told in _____

2. _____ bring the story to life for readers.

Student Model

1. The first event Theon describes is: _____

_____

2. List two sensory details that Theon includes in the first body paragraph.

• _____

• _____

Conclusion

The **conclusion** sums up the event and why _____
_____

Student Model | Theon sums up the event by stating: _____

_____

_____

Brainstorm

▶ Read the writing prompt. Then use the boxes to help you brainstorm writing ideas.

At School

With Your Friends

Writing Prompt:
Write a personal narrative essay about a turning point in your life.

With Your Family

Other Turning Points

Choose Your Topic

▶ Select one of your ideas from the idea web. Then complete the sentences.

I plan to write about _____

This experience taught me _____

_____

Organize Ideas for Writing

▶ **Complete this outline with notes for your personal narrative.**

I. Introduction Introduce your experience and the lesson it taught you.

Topic: _____

_____

Point of View: _____

_____

II. Body Decide what part of the story each body paragraph will describe. Then list specific and sensory details that bring the story to life.

A. Part of Story: _____

_____

    Detail 1: _____

_____

    Detail 2: _____

_____

B. Part of Story: _____

_____

    Detail 1: _____

_____

    Detail 2: _____

_____

C. Part of Story: _____

_____

    Detail 1: _____

_____

    Detail 2: _____

_____

III. Conclusion Summarize the experience and why it is important to you.

This experience taught me _____

_____

Write Your Draft

▶ **Write a draft of your personal narrative.**

Writing Prompt:
Write a personal narrative essay about a turning point in your life.

WORD CHOICES	
Everyday	**Precise**
change	reform, transform
help	assist, support
live	survive
real	genuine

_____
(title of narrative)

Introduction

▶ **Write your introductory statement. Engage the reader by establishing a point of view.**

_____

_____

_____

_____

_____

_____

▶ **Type your introduction on the computer or write it on paper. Then use these transition words and phrases to help you complete a draft of your personal narrative.**

Body

At first, . . .	After that, . . .
To start with, . . .	Consequently, . . .
It all started when . . .	Even though, . . .
Eventually, . . .	Finally, . . .
Then, . . .	In the end, . . .

Conclusion

Looking back now, I . . .	From now on, . . .
This experience taught me . . .	The next time . . .

Revise Your Personal Narrative

▶ **Evaluate:** Rate your personal narrative. Then have a writing partner rate it.

Scoring Guide

needs improvement	average	good	excellent
1	2	3	4

1. UNDERLINE the introductory statement. Does it identify the topic and engage the reader?

Self   1   2   3   4
Partner   1   2   3   4

2. NUMBER the events in time order. Are the events in the correct order?

Self   1   2   3   4
Partner   1   2   3   4

3. ✔CHECK the sensory details. Do they bring the story to life?

Self   1   2   3   4
Partner   1   2   3   4

4. BOX the dialogue. Does it sound realistic?

Self   1   2   3   4
Partner   1   2   3   4

5. CIRCLE transition words and phrases. Do they connect ideas?

Self   1   2   3   4
Partner   1   2   3   4

6. DOUBLE UNDERLINE vivid adjectives. Are they precise words?

Self   1   2   3   4
Partner   1   2   3   4

7. ★STAR the conclusion. Does it sum up why the experience is important?

Self   1   2   3   4
Partner   1   2   3   4

▶ **Discuss:** Give feedback on your partner's personal narrative essay.

1. Start with positive comments about your partner's personal narrative.

A strong part of your narrative is _____

_____

_____

I enjoyed reading the part in which you

_____

_____

2. Give your partner suggestions for revision.

I have a question about _____

_____

The sensory details need _____

_____

The dialogue needs _____

_____

3. Answer any questions your partner has about your suggestions.

4. Ask your partner for feedback. Use the frames below to summarize your partner's feedback.

A strong part of my narrative was . . .
You had a question about . . .
My sensory details need . . .
My narrative needs . . .

▶ **Revise** Now revise your personal narrative.

Grammar USING ADVERBS

An **adjective** describes a person, place, or thing. An **adverb** describes a verb, an adjective, or another adverb. Many adverbs end in *-ly*.

- **Use adverbs to make your writing more precise.**

Example

Adjective	Adverb
I was **patient** with the new student.	I waited **patiently** for the new student.
Jonathan was **slow** at making friends.	Jonathan made friends **slowly**.
We are always **careful** on the train.	We stepped **carefully** onto the train.

▶ **Circle the adverbs in the sentences below.**

1. Poetry changed Ekiwah's life [dramatic / dramatically].

2. He felt [absolutely / absolute] positive that his life was better.

3. Waila and Dali reacted [different / differently] to their mom's imprisonment.

4. Waila never told anyone what [really / real] happened.

5. She tried to deal [quietly / quiet] with her problems.

6. Jonathan's grades dropped [quick / quickly] after he moved to the U.S.

▶ **Rewrite the sentences by changing the adjectives to adverbs.**

7. Being a new student was <u>fair</u> difficult for Jonathan.

_____

_____

8. He tried <u>desperate</u> to make new friends.

_____

_____

9. He took his education <u>serious</u>, and his grades began to improve.

_____

_____

10. The teens had <u>slight</u> different attitudes about their personal challenges.

_____

_____

▶ **Edit Your Draft.** Take a close look at the sentences in your draft. **Do they use adverbs correctly?** Fix the ones that do not.

Mechanics USING QUOTATION MARKS

Quotation marks show the exact words of a speaker.

- The first word of a quotation is capitalized.
- Punctuation usually goes inside the ending quotation mark.

Example

Correct	Incorrect
Lisa yelled, "Way to go!"	Lisa yelled, "way to go!"
Josue said, "You did it!"	Josue said, "You did it"!

▶ **Find and correct five errors in this paragraph.**

Student Model

> Living with my cousin Rhondi has taught me to appreciate life. Rhondi is blind, and she came to live with my family last year. She is like most teenagers, but her life has been full of chalenges. Once, she told me that people always yell at her because they think she can't hear. She said, I just tell them that I'm only blind—not def. The interesting thing about Rhondi is her great sense of humor. I learned from her how to be easygoing and how not to take everything so serious!

CHECK AND CORRECT

- ☐ <u>UNDERLINE</u> one error with an adverb.
- ☐ Insert two missing quotation marks.
- ☐ (CIRCLE) two spelling errors and correct them.

▶ **Edit Your Draft.** Look at the sentences in your own draft. **Do they all use quotation marks correctly?** Fix the ones that do not.

Final Draft/Present

▶ **Write a final draft of your essay on the computer or on paper. Check it again and correct any errors before you present it.**

Focus Skill | Find a Mentor

Evaluate an Application

A mentor is an older or more experienced person who helps someone younger or less experienced reach his or her career goals.

▶ **Read this application to a youth mentoring program. Then answer the questions below.**

HELP A TEEN MENTOR PROGRAM APPLICATION

Share your experience and talents with a teen who needs a mentor.

Mercer, Terrance — 32 — Computer Programmer

Name (last, first) — Age — Profession

tmercer@example.com — 206-555-1234

Email Address — Telephone

Why do you want to be a mentor? A mentor taught me computer programming as a teen. That helped me get a job after high school. I would like to be a mentor and help a young teen be successful.

What skills could you teach a teenager? Basic and C++ computer coding, guitar playing, cooking

Do you have a criminal record? ☐ yes ☒ no — If yes, please explain on the reverse side.

1 What is Terrance Mercer's job?
Ⓐ mentor
Ⓑ teacher
Ⓒ musician
Ⓓ computer programmer

2 Why does Terrance want to be a mentor?
Ⓐ He wants to teach teens music.
Ⓑ He wants to get paid.
Ⓒ He learned a lot from a mentor when he was a teenager.
Ⓓ He has a criminal record and wants to do something good.

3 Would Terrance be a good mentor for a teenager? Why or why not?

_____

_____

_____

_____

_____

_____

Police Officer
Adele Rios

This officer investigates crimes—and connects with young people.

▶ **Read the interview and job information. Then answer the questions below about Adele Rios's job.**

S **Scholastic: What do you do on the job?**

Adele Rios: I investigate crimes that involve students, such as drugs or child abuse. I also work in schools teaching students about gangs and bullying. I call the class "Juvenile Law 101." I want young adults to know their rights and responsibilities.

S **What happens when you have to arrest a student you know?**

I tell the student, "Even good kids make mistakes. I am arresting you now, but I will see you in the future under friendlier circumstances." I want students to learn from their mistakes and take a better path. Mostly, I want them to stay in school and get something out of it!

S **Mentors can help students learn valuable skills and stay out of trouble. How can teens find good mentors?**

My teachers and coaches were my mentors. They motivated me to stay in school. I encourage kids to pursue their interests and to find adults who are supportive and interested in similar things.

1 **What makes Adele Rios an effective mentor for the students she works with? Explain.**

_____

_____

_____

2 **How important is Rios's job to her community? Mark the line.**

1　2　3　4　5

Not very important　　　Very important

3 **I think Rios's job is/isn't (circle one) important to her community because** _____

_____

ON THE JOB

LOCATION
Hillsboro, Oregon

EDUCATION
Associate's degree in Criminology

RESPONSIBILITIES
- Investigates crimes
- Writes reports
- Teaches classes

SKILLS
- Listening to all sides of an issue
- Solving problems
- Explaining the law to teens
- Showing fairness and compassion

SALARY
$35,000–$60,000

TOOLS OF THE TRADE
"Speaking another language is a great tool for my work. I can connect with Spanish-speaking students."

CAREER CONNECTION

Law Enforcement
www.careerclusters.org

Related Jobs
- police detective
- private investigator
- lawyer

Focus Skills | Set Criteria | Ask Questions

How can I find a mentor?

A mentor is someone who can help you set and reach goals. Complete an application to find a mentor for yourself.

❶ Collaborate. Brainstorm specific ways a mentor could help you.

Challenges/Questions	Mentor Support
At School:	
Job and Career:	
Personal Life:	

❷ Set criteria. What qualities would you look for in a good mentor?

- ❑ has interesting career
- ❑ smart
- ❑ ambitious
- ❑ athletic
- ❑ kind
- ❑ artistically talented
- ❑ casual
- ❑ calm
- ❑ patient
- ❑ funny
- ❑ thoughtful
- ❑ energetic

What other criteria should a mentor meet?

- _____
- _____
- _____

❸ Complete the application.

MENTOR MATCH-UP

Choose from thousands of interesting, fun professionals who want to be YOUR mentor. Complete this form to help us match you with a mentor who can help you reach your goals!

_____   _____   _____
Name (last, first)   Age   Grade

_____   _____
Parent/Guardian Name   Home Phone

1. What personal qualities do you hope your mentor will have?

- _____

- _____

- _____

2. We have mentors with a wide range of professions and jobs. List three jobs or careers that interest you.

- _____

- _____

- _____

3. Describe an issue that a mentor could help you with. How do you think the mentor could support you?

_____

_____

_____

4. What else is important for us to know about you before we match you with your mentor?

_____

_____

_____

_____

Comprehension

▶ **Fill in the circle next to the correct answer.**

1. How was Jonathan's social life different at his new school in the United States?

 Ⓐ He had more trouble making friends at his new school.

 Ⓑ It was easier to find people he liked at his new school.

 Ⓒ He became popular way faster at his new school.

 Ⓓ He had just a few really good friends at the new school.

<table>
<tr><td>

Here's a Tip.

Read over your answers carefully. Double-check that you filled in the answers in the correct places.

</td></tr>
</table>

CRITICAL READING

2. Analyze: How was Ekiwah able to face his challenges successfully?

 Ⓐ He forced other people to take care of him.

 Ⓑ He isolated himself from the world because of his diseases.

 Ⓒ He learned to express himself and share his talent with the world.

 Ⓓ He left his small Mexican village and went to live in New York City.

3. In what ways are Waila and Dali different from each other?

 Ⓐ They were both born in the Dominican Republic.

 Ⓑ Their mom worked 12 hours a day to make ends meet.

 Ⓒ They reacted differently when their mom went to jail.

 Ⓓ They both care about their mother.

4. When did Waila and Dali feel closest to their mother?

 Ⓐ right before their mom went to prison

 Ⓑ before they moved back to the Dominican Republic

 Ⓒ after they graduated from high school

 Ⓓ after their mom went to prison

CRITICAL READING

5. Synthesize: What message do the three readings in this Workshop share?

 Ⓐ A good attitude and lots of effort can get you through tough times.

 Ⓑ Family members may not always be there to support you.

 Ⓒ Moving to a new country can mean new social problems.

 Ⓓ Life's turning points are easier when they come as a surprise.

Vocabulary

▶ **Fill in the circle next to the correct definition of the underlined word.**

1. Were you <u>involved</u> in planning the pregame meeting?

   Ⓐ included   Ⓒ applauded

   Ⓑ ignored   Ⓓ offended

2. Hector <u>persisted</u> at working on his comic book, though he had an after-school job.

   Ⓐ refused to do something   Ⓒ continued doing something

   Ⓑ enjoyed doing something   Ⓓ appreciated something

3. I am <u>positive</u> that a high school diploma will make a <u>dramatic</u> change in my life.

   Ⓐ unhappy / dangerous   Ⓒ delighted / successful

   Ⓑ very sure / large and exciting Ⓓ doubtful / risky and unlucky

▶ **Choose the word with the correct noun ending to complete this sentence.**

4. The boys' _____ about the sport changed once they started winning games.

   Ⓐ attitudeses   Ⓒ attitudes

   Ⓑ attitude   Ⓓ attitudies

▶ **Use context clues to choose the correct definition of the underlined word.**

5. Terry had so many options for dessert, he found himself in a <u>dilemma</u>; he had to choose, but he didn't want to.

   Ⓐ happy situation   Ⓒ options

   Ⓑ food illness   Ⓓ difficult choice

Short Answer

CRITICAL READING ▶ **Evaluate:** Use what you've read in this Workshop to answer the question below. Check your spelling and grammar.

Which person in this Workshop do you most admire? Why?

_____

_____

_____

_____

WORKSHOP 9

INFORMATIONAL TEXT

Literary Text

COMPREHENSION FOCUS
Make Inferences

CRITICAL READING FOCUS
Analyze
Synthesize
Evaluate

Reading 1 Heartbeat of Harlem |
Nonfiction Article

Reading 2 from *Bad Boy* | **Memoir**

Reading 3 Langston Hughes's Harlem | **Poetry**

THE STREETS OF HARLEM

It all began in the 1920s. Harlem was becoming the heartbeat of African-American culture. The streets were filled with excitement. Jazz musicians played the blues. Artists splashed colors onto canvas. Writers like Langston Hughes wrote poetry about being African American and living in Harlem. Other writers like Walter Dean Myers were growing up on its streets.

Take a walk back in time . . . on the streets of Harlem.

Academic Vocabulary

Target Word	Meaning	Examples
► Read the Target Words. Rate each one using the scale below.*	► Read the Target Word meanings. Write in the missing words.	► Finish the Target Word examples below. Write in the missing ones.
agony (p. 238) ag•o•ny (noun) ① ② ③ ④	great _____ or suffering	• _____ can cause **agony**. • _____ _____
inquiry (p. 238) in•quir•y (noun) ① ② ③ ④	a question	• An **inquiry** I hear often is _____ • _____ _____
universal (p. 240) u•ni•ver•sal (adjective) ① ② ③ ④	concerning all the members of a group or of the _____	Music is a **universal** language.
incident (p. 242) in•ci•dent (noun) ① ② ③ ④	an event	• An **incident** that I don't want to be a part of is _____ • _____ _____
minor (p. 244) mi•nor (adjective) ① ② ③ ④	less important or less _____	• _____ is a **minor** mistake. • _____ _____

*Rating Scale
① = I don't know the word.　③ = I think I know the word.
② = I've seen it or heard it.　④ = I know it and use it.

The Key Idea

▶ **WRITE** What is this article mostly about?

_____

_____

VOCABULARY
Target Word

resident

res•i•dent (noun)

Rate It: ① ② ③ ④

Meaning

someone who _____

in a particular place

Example

I've been a **resident** of

_____

_____

React and Write

▶ **WRITE** What is the most interesting thing you learned about Harlem? Why is it interesting?

Summarize

In one or two sentences, summarize what happened during the Harlem Renaissance. Include the topic and important details.

Heartbeat of Harlem

by Sierra Gordon

Harlem is a large neighborhood in the northern part of Manhattan in New York City. From the 1920s to 1950s, Harlem's **residents** included many great African-American writers, musicians, and artists. They made Harlem famous through their writing, music, and art.

In the early 1900s, many African Americans moved from the South to the North. They were escaping racist laws and poverty. There were also more job options in the North. This movement was called the Great Migration.

Many people who came north settled in Harlem. By the 1920s and 1930s, Harlem had become the center of African-American culture. That time period is known as the Harlem Renaissance. Painters and photographers captured images of the streets. Writers like Langston Hughes put new ideas to paper. And singers like Ella Fitzgerald belted out the blues at the famous Apollo Theater.

Music and dancing have always been a big part of Harlem life.

Today, Harlem has something for everyone. Jazz and blues fill the air. Restaurants serve delicious Southern-style soul food. And neighborhood parks are filled with the dribbling beat of basketball games. In fact, the Harlem Globetrotters basketball team has been around for 80 years. They've slam-dunked their way through more than 25,000 games!

Throughout its history, Harlem has had its ups and downs. But today, it's still one of the most exciting places in the world. END

Words to Know! **renaissance** rebirth

Comprehension Focus

Make Inferences

When you **make inferences** you form ideas about things that are not directly stated in the text. To make inferences:

- Look for a situation in the text in which the author gives clues but doesn't state exactly what is happening.
- Think about what you already know about the topic or events.
- Combine the text clues with your own experiences or knowledge to make an inference.

▶ **Complete this chart to make an inference about "Heartbeat of Harlem."**

What I Learned From Reading

In the early 1900s, many African Americans moved from the South to escape racist laws and poverty.

What I Already Know

My Inference

Active Reading

▶ **WRITE** Who is Crazy Johnny?

_____

_____

Craft and Structure

Setting is where and when a narrative's action takes place. This memoir section is set in Harlem in the 1940s or early 1950s.

✔ **CHECK** Mark four details that describe the setting.

CRITICAL READING

Analyze

1. CIRCLE What does Myers write about downtown cabs in Harlem?

2. ▶ **WRITE** What does this tell you about Harlem in the 1940s and 1950s?

_____

_____

_____

_____

 ## React and Write

▶ **WRITE** How would you describe your own neighborhood?

from **BAD**

BOY

by Walter Dean Myers

Walter Dean Myers is a famous author. He grew up in Harlem in the 1940s and 1950s. In this excerpt from his memoir, Myers learns a very painful lesson.

1. <u>UNDERLINE</u> Mark a detail about where Walter plays.

2. ▶ **WRITE** What do you know about open spaces in cities and urban areas?

_____

_____

_____

_____

PART I

I lived on Morningside Avenue, but I played mostly on the side streets because that's where the sewers were. The sewers were bases if you played stickball, they were the goal lines if you played football, they were base if you played tag, they were the spot you made your first shot from if you played skullies. The side street between Morningside Avenue and Manhattan Avenue was a pleasant block, lined with brownstones that had been converted into either single-room occupancies with community bathrooms or, at least, apartment dwellings that contained between four and six families. . . .

3. ▶ **WRITE** What can you infer about why Walter and his friends play in the streets?

_____

_____

_____

_____

Craft and Structure

Irony is the contrast between what readers expect and what actually happens. An example of irony is that Crazy Johnny's name makes readers expect him to be mean and insane. Actually, the opposite is true.

The whole block was guarded by Crazy Johnny, who had returned from the war kind of shell-shocked. If anything went wrong, Crazy Johnny would try to set it right. This usually meant trying to stop fights between kids and sweeping up broken bottles.

We didn't get many yellow cabs coming to the street, because downtown cabs didn't stop for black people and you didn't need to use a cab when the A train came directly to Harlem. One day in May there weren't any kids on the block to play with. ➤

▶ **WRITE** How is Crazy Johnny different from what his name might make you expect? Use evidence from the text in your response.

_____

_____

_____

_____

Words to Know!	**converted** made into something else

Active Reading

▶**WRITE** What does Walter do when he gets home?

_____

_____

_____

VOCABULARY
Target Word

manage

man•age (verb)

Rate It: ① ② ③ ④

Meaning

to be able to do something that is _____

Example

If I miss the bus, I might manage to get to school by

_____

React and Write

▶**WRITE** Do you think Walter should have told his mother what happened? Why or why not?

"My jeans were in shreds at the knees, and the blood from my scraped knees was showing through. I tried to sit on the church steps, but the pain was too great."

A yellow cab pulled up in front of a building, and a fairly elegant-looking lady got out. For some reason I thought it would be a good idea to hitch a ride on the back bumper of the cab. The cab started off with a jerk, and I was thrown off the bumper, but the sleeve of my shirt was caught. I was dragged the entire length of the block, bouncing along behind the cab, past the sewers, past parked cars, and all the way to the corner, where the cab was stopped by a light. It was there that I unhooked my sleeve and **managed** to get to my feet.

The agony was excruciating. Clyde asked me if I was hurt, and I said no.

"Your pants are torn," he said.

My jeans were in shreds at the knees, and the blood from my scraped knees was showing through. I tried to sit on the church steps, but the pain was too great. Stiff-leggedly I made my way around the corner and over to my building.

When I got home, Mama was on the phone and I went into the bathroom and got the iodine. Then I went to my room, stopping only to answer my mother's inquiry as to whether or not I was hungry.

The iodine had a stopper and a glass rod applicator. I touched some iodine to my scraped leg. _Yow!_ Enough of that. I went directly to bed. ➤

Words to Know! | **excruciating** extremely painful

Comprehension Focus
Make Inferences

▶ **Complete this chart to make inferences about Part I of "Bad Boy."**

What I Learned From Reading

Walter thought it would be a good idea to jump on the back of a cab.

What I Already Know

My Inference

What I Learned From Reading

Walter told both Clyde and his mother that nothing was wrong.

What I Already Know

My Inference

Active Reading

★STAR How does Walter's mother react to his injuries?

VOCABULARY
 Target Word

reverse

re•verse (verb)

Rate It: ① ② ③ ④

Meaning

to change to the _____

position

Example

Someone might **reverse** a car's direction to _____

_____

 Craft and Structure

Sensory details describe how things look, sound, feel, smell, or taste. Writers use sensory details to create vivid images in the reader's mind.

✔CHECK Mark two sensory details from the text that show how severe Myers's injuries were.

 React and Write

▶WRITE What do you think of the way Walter's mother handled the situation?

PART II

When Mama called me for supper that evening, I called back that I wasn't hungry. She called me a second time and told me to come to the kitchen, where my father now sat at the table, his dinner before him. By that time my legs had stiffened so I could hardly walk.

"What's wrong with you, boy?" my father asked.

"Nothing." My universal answer.

"What's wrong with you, boy?" My father's voice again, deeper, more resolute.

"My legs hurt," I said.

"Take your pants down."

Right there at the dinner table. I had changed pants and now undid my belt and gingerly let the changed pants down. My mother gasped when she saw my legs—a mass of bruises, swelling, and dried blood.

"What happened to you?" my father demanded.

I knew that hitching a ride on the back of a cab was wrong. And I had been trying so hard all year to be good. Maybe all these things were swimming around in my head too quickly. I honestly don't know what made me answer the way I did.

"Mama beat me with a stick," I said, the tears already flowing.

I think that if my mama hadn't been so shocked at the condition of my legs, she might have been able to respond. As it was, I don't think that she could really believe what she was hearing. First, there was her darling boy come home a bruised and bloody mess, in itself enough to send her into a blind panic, and then the same darling boy claiming to have suffered his injuries at her hand.

| Words to Know! | **resolute** feeling strong and certain about something |

Maybe I could have **reversed** myself, admitted what had really happened, if my father had not gone absolutely crazy with anger. He bellowed, "If you ever . . . how . . . why . . . If you ever touch him again I'll . . . " My father sputtered on and on. At this point Mama was crying. I was gingerly put into a hot bath to let my legs soak. I sat in the hot water and listened as my father hollered at Mama. It never occurred to him that I could be lying about such a thing. I went to bed and told God I was sorry.

The next two days I couldn't go to school. Mama brought me food and put it on a chair near my bed. She didn't say anything to me, just looked at me as if she had never seen me before. ➤

"I knew that hitching a ride on the back of a cab was wrong. And I had been trying so hard all year to be good. Maybe all these things were swimming around in my head too quickly."

Make Inferences

1. **UNDERLINE** What does Walter say about how he got hurt?

2. ▶ **WRITE** How would you react if someone accused you of something you didn't do?

_____

_____

_____

_____

3. ▶ **WRITE** Walter's mother cries but stays silent. How might she be feeling about what Walter says?

_____

_____

_____

REVIEW
Compare and Contrast

1. **CIRCLE** How does Walter's father react to the explanation about the accident?

2. ▶ **WRITE** How does Walter's mother react to the explanation and to Walter's father's anger?

_____

_____

_____

_____

Active Reading

 WRITE What does Walter do when a foul ball lands on the roof?

_____

_____

Target Word

 instruct

in•struct (verb)

Rate It: ① ② ③ ④

Meaning

to _____

Example

Parents might **instruct** their children to _____

_____

Evaluate

 WRITE Do you think Walter's mother should have forgiven him? Why or why not?

_____

_____

_____

_____

React and Write

WRITE Describe a time when someone forgave you for something you did wrong. How did you feel?

PART III

Two weeks later I was as good as new. Mama had been **instructed** by my dad not to touch me, and by the redness in his eyes she knew he meant it. I avoided _her_ eyes when she asked how I could do such a thing to her. When she asked me what had really happened, I didn't answer. But Mama forgave me as usual, and I focused instead on the coming graduation from the sixth grade. My father checked my legs once a week because he hadn't forgotten the incident. Neither had God.

Eight days before graduation. We were playing stickball on 122nd Street, and a foul ball went up on the flat roof over the church vestibule. There was a drainpipe that came from the main roof and down the

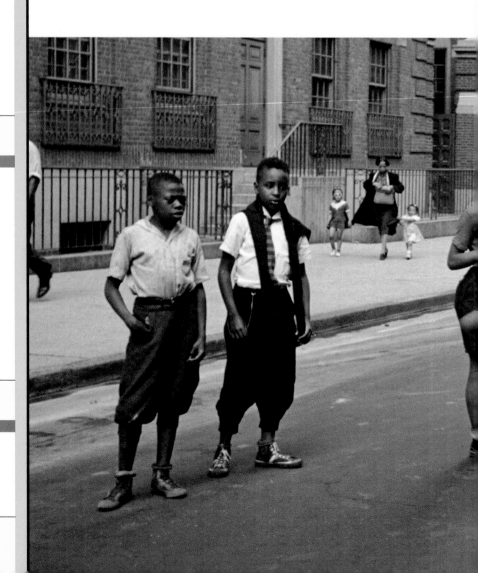

side of the church. Reverend Abbott, when he had been at the church the summer before, had put barbed wire on the pipe to keep us from climbing it to get balls that went up there. We had ripped the wire down, and every kid on the block, girls included, could climb onto that roof. Up I went after the foul ball.

Enter Crazy Johnny.

"Get down from there!" he half yelled, half growled in his Crazy Johnny kind of way.

I threw the ball down, but I didn't come down. What I did instead was taunt Crazy Johnny from my perch. Johnny knew about the drainpipe and started climbing up after me. What Johnny didn't know was that I had a plan. ➤

| Words to Know! | **perch** | a high place |

Make Inferences

1. **UNDERLINE** Walter's mother asks how he could have done such a thing. Mark a detail that shows Walter's reaction.

2. ▶ **WRITE** What do you know about how people act when they feel guilty?

_____

_____

3. ▶ **WRITE** How is Walter feeling about what happened?

_____

_____

Craft and Structure

Characterization is how an author tells readers about a character. An author can tell about a character by:

• describing the character's appearance, thoughts, or actions.

• telling what others think about the character.

Walter climbs up the drainpipe even though he knows it is risky. This characterization tells readers that he is not afraid of danger.

1. What words or phrases would you use to describe Crazy Johnny?

_____

_____

2. (CIRCLE) Mark a detail that supports your response.

Active Reading

★ **STAR** How does Walter get off the roof?

VOCABULARY
Target Word

sustain

sus•tain (verb)

Rate It: ① ② ③ ④

Meaning

_to _____ something_

Example

A boxer might **sustain** a

_____

during a match.

React and Write

▶ **WRITE** Do you think Walter should have told his parents that he jumped off the roof? Why or why not?

Make Inferences

What details show Walter's personality as an adventurous risk taker?

Eric and I had watched enough war movies to know that if we ever got into the army, we were going to go airborne. Jumping out of a plane was fairly easy. You jumped, your parachute opened, and you floated down. In order not to hurt yourself on landing, you bent your knees, landed on your heels, and fell to one side.

Up came Crazy Johnny. My friends below screamed. I waited by the edge of the roof of the one-story building. I let Johnny get halfway across the roof before I jumped, my legs together and slightly bent. I landed on my heels, and the pain was unbearable.

Patty Lee and John Lightbourne, friends who lived on Morningside Avenue, helped me to the church steps, where I sat for a while before going home. I wanted desperately to tell somebody about the pain in my heels, but what could I say so soon after lying about the first incident? Oh, yes, I jumped off a roof? Mama beat me on the heels with a stick? I suffered in silence for the next two weeks. Years later I found out I had **sustained** minor fractures to both feet. END

TEXT FEATURE Reading a Map

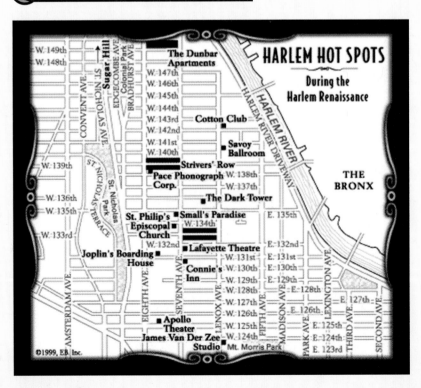

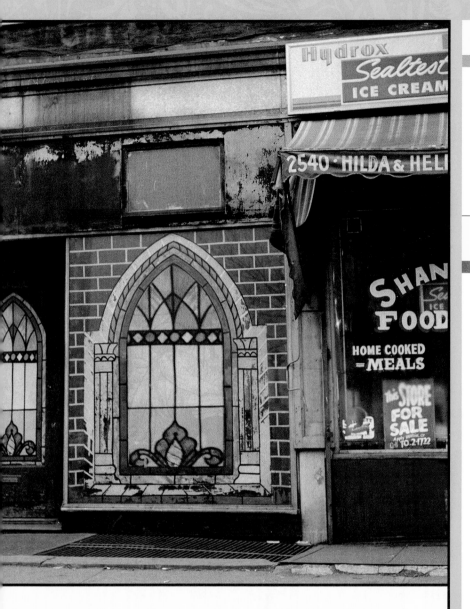

A neighborhood map shows the location of streets.

① What information does this map show?

Ⓐ New York City in 1999

Ⓑ the state of New York

Ⓒ Harlem during the Harlem Renaissance

Ⓓ what Harlem will look like in the future

② What river runs along the east side of Harlem?

_____

③ **Analyze:** Why are the hot spots so close together?

_____

_____

Draw Conclusions

▶ **WRITE** Based on Walter's two accidents, what conclusion can you draw about him?

_____

_____

Skills Check

1. (**CIRCLE**) Mark two details that tell how Walter might be feeling about what he has done.

2. ▶ **WRITE** How does it feel to admit you did something wrong?

_____

_____

3. ▶ **WRITE** Why does Walter decide not to tell about his painful injury?

_____

_____

_____

Meet the Author

WALTER DEAN MYERS
Born: 1937 in Martinsburg, West Virginia

Childhood: His mother died when Myers was two. He moved to New York City and was raised by foster parents in Harlem. In school, he struggled with a speech problem. He misbehaved and got into a lot of trouble.

Awards: Coretta Scott King Award; Newbery Honor

Famous Works: *Bad Boy, Harlem, Slam!, Monster*

Active Reading

★**STAR** Whom is the speaker of the first poem addressing?

CRITICAL READING
Synthesize

▶**WRITE** What new metaphor could you add to "Dreams"? Finish the lines below with a metaphor that works with the poem.

Hold fast to dreams
For if dreams fail
Life is _____

_____

_____

React and Write

▶**WRITE** Which poem do you like best? Why?

Meet the Author

LANGSTON HUGHES
Born: 1902 in Joplin, Missouri

Work Life: In the seventh grade, Hughes got a job cleaning a hotel near his school. In the eighth grade, he wrote his first poem. But his father said that writing wouldn't pay bills. He never gave up writing, and published his first book in 1926 at age 24.

His Legacy: As an adult, Hughes moved to Harlem, where he wrote poetry, plays, and short stories, and listened to jazz music. He is widely considered one of the most important American writers of the 20th century.

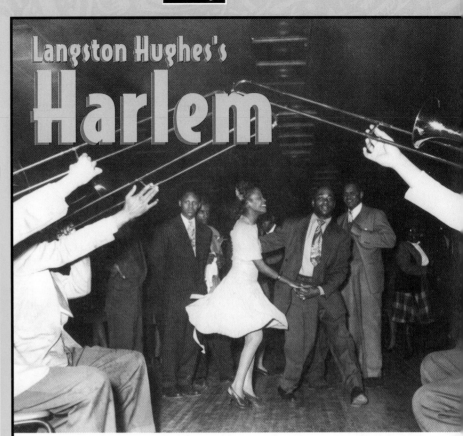

Langston Hughes's Harlem

Langston Hughes was a writer whose poetry was an important part of the Harlem Renaissance. What do his poems say about Harlem?

Juke Box Love Song

I could take the Harlem night

and wrap around you,

Take the neon lights and make a crown,

Take the Lenox Avenue busses,

Taxis, subways,

And for your love song tone their rumble down.

Take Harlem's heartbeat,

Make a drumbeat,

Put it on a record, let it whirl,

And while we listen to it play,

Dance with you till day—

Dance with you, my sweet brown Harlem girl.

Harlem [2]

What happens to a dream deferred?

Does it dry up

like a raisin in the sun?

Or fester like a sore—

And then run?

Does it stink like rotten meat?

Or crust and sugar over—

like a syrupy sweet?

Maybe it just sags

like a heavy load.

Or does it explode?

Dreams

Hold fast to dreams

For if dreams die

Life is a broken-winged bird

That cannot fly.

Hold fast to dreams

For when dreams go

Life is a barren field

Frozen with snow. END

Words to Know!   **deferred**   delayed

Craft and Structure

A **simile** is a comparison of two unlike things, using the words *like* or *as*. In "Harlem [2]," one simile is: "like a raisin in the sun."

1. CIRCLE Mark two other similes in that poem.

2. ▶ WRITE Why do you think the poet uses these similes?

_____

_____

_____

_____

_____

_____

A **metaphor** is a comparison in which something is said to be something else. Metaphors use *is* or *was*. In "Dreams," one metaphor is: "Life is a broken-winged bird."

3. UNDERLINE Find another metaphor in that poem.

4. ▶ WRITE What is Langston Hughes's message about dreams?

_____

_____

_____

_____

_____

Word Challenge

start

1 **Think about it.** Which decision would *your parents* want you to **reverse**?

☐ organizing your room

☐ not studying for a test

☐ eating a whole pizza

☐ getting a part-time job

2 **Tell it.** Have you ever been *really* surprised or scared? What was the **incident**?

_____

_____

_____

_____

_____

_____

3 Multiple-Meaning Words

Multiple-Meaning Words are words that have more than one meaning. Example: *minor* means "less important or less serious." But it also means "someone younger than adult age."

Complete these sentences with *jam, stuff,* or *present.*

There's a **minor** problem. You're still a **minor**.

1. Don't wait for the future. Do it now, in the _____.

2. The garage is full of _____.

3. Here is your birthday _____.

4. Let's get some guitars and _____.

5. We will _____ my brother's *piñata* with his favorite candy.

6. Do you want some _____ on your toast?

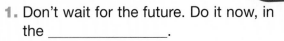

I can't wait to tell my friends about this **incident**!

4 **Express yourself.** If I could **manage** to save enough money, I would buy

_____

_____

_____

5 Name them. Name three other **residents** on your block.

someone your age: _____

someone who lives next door: _____

someone who has a pet: _____

6 Check it. Which would cause you the most **agony**?

- ☐ a terrible headache
- ☐ a bad hair day
- ☐ a broken bone
- ☐ a math test

This is the worst headache I've ever had. I'm in **agony**!

7 Rate them. Read the **inquiries** below. How often do you hear them?

1 = a lot
2 = sometimes
3 = never

____ "When will you be home?"

____ "What time is it?"

____ "Did you finish your homework?"

____ "Can I borrow a dollar?"

____ "Are you mad at me?"

8 Latin Roots

Our group has a **universal** goal. We want to **unite** all of the **universe**.

A **root** is a word or word part from another language that is the basis of an English word. The word *universal* comes from the Latin root *unus*, which means "one."

Complete these sentences with *unicycle*, *uniform*, or *unique*.

1. I could tell she was a firefighter because she was wearing a _____.
2. A _____ is harder to ride than a bicycle.
3. That painting is _____.

9 Think about it. You need help. Who could **instruct** you in:

cooking a meal? _____

fixing a bicycle? _____

fixing a computer problem? _____

10 Describe it. Write a caption for the photo below. Use the word **sustain**.

_____

_____

_____

finish

Writing Text Type
Research Paper

A **research paper** presents information on a subject from multiple authoritative sources.

▶ Read student Amy Chin's research paper about the similarities and differences between child labor in the U.S. and around the world.

Introduction

The **introductory statement** introduces the topic of the research paper.

1. UNDERLINE the introductory statement.

A **thesis statement** tells what the writer will explain about the topic.

2. BOX the thesis statement.

Body

Each body paragraph starts with a **topic sentence** that includes a **controlling idea** about the topic.

3. UNDERLINE the topic sentence in each body paragraph.

4. BOX each controlling idea.

Facts and evidence support the writer's thesis.

5. ✔ CHECK six facts and pieces of evidence.

The writer **cites** multiple **sources**.

6. CIRCLE four source citations.

Conclusion

The **conclusion** sums up the writer's ideas about the research topic.

7. ★ STAR the conclusion.

Student Model

An International Problem
by Amy Chin

Child labor is a global problem. Child laborers around the world face poverty, long hours, and work that is dangerous and difficult.

Internationally, children who must earn a living work long hours. For example, Muhammad picks tea leaves in India. He works more than 16 hours a day (Marquez 99). James also works long hours, picking crops in Ohio. This 14-year-old labors nine hours a day, six days a week (Rosenberg 94).

Child workers often perform grueling, dangerous work. For example, James carries 50-pound bags of produce in sweltering heat while working the farms in Ohio (Rosenberg 95). In Indonesia, Tariah often cuts her hands as she picks through garbage dumps looking for materials for her boss to sell (Saks 92).

Worldwide, child workers endure long hours of painful labor to help their families. Tariah gives all her earnings to her parents (Saks 92). Likewise, James's income helps to support his family (Rosenberg 96).

In conclusion, child laborers live in many different nations and do different jobs, but they all face similar problems and difficulties: poverty, long hours, dangerous conditions, and low pay.

Analyze the Text Type

▶ **Work with a partner to understand the purpose and form of a research paper.**

Purpose: Research Paper

The purpose of a research paper is to _____

_____

Introduction

The **introductory paragraph** of a research paper includes:

1. an _____ that introduces the _____

2. a _____ that explains how _____

_____

Student Model | In her introduction, Amy Chin:

1. introduces the topic of her research paper, which is: _____

2. includes a thesis statement, which is: _____

_____

Body

The **body paragraphs** give specific information to support the writer's thesis.

1. Each paragraph starts with a _____

2. Facts and evidence from _____ and _____ sources support the thesis.

Student Model | In the first body paragraph, Chin:

1. begins with a topic sentence, which is: _____

_____

2. includes these two pieces of facts and evidence:

   • _____

   • _____

Conclusion

The **conclusion** sums up the writer's _____.

Student Model | Chin sums up her ideas by stating that _____

_____

Prewrite

Writing Prompt:

Write a research paper about the similarities and differences between life during the Harlem Renaissance and life today.

▶ **Take Notes: Review the readings in Workshop 9. Gather facts and evidence about the topic from multiple sources.**

Source 1: _____

Source 2: _____

Source 3: _____

State Your Topic

▶ **Use your notes to help you state the topic. Complete the sentences below.**

I plan to write about _____

I will explore _____

_____

Organize Ideas for Writing

▶ **Complete this outline with notes for your research paper.**

I. Introduction State your topic and your thesis.

Topic: _____

Thesis: _____

_____

II. Body Write a topic sentence for each body paragraph that supports your thesis. Then list facts and evidence that support the topic sentence.

A. Topic Sentence 1: _____

_____

Fact/Evidence 1: _____

_____

Fact/Evidence 2: _____

_____

B. Topic Sentence 2: _____

_____

Fact/Evidence 1: _____

_____

Fact/Evidence 2: _____

_____

C. Topic Sentence 3: _____

_____

Fact/Evidence 1: _____

_____

Fact/Evidence 2: _____

_____

III. Conclusion Sum up your ideas about the research topic.

From my research, _____

_____

_____

Write Your Draft

▶ **Write a draft of your research paper.**

Writing Prompt:
Write a research paper about the similarities and differences between life during the Harlem Renaissance and life today.

WORD CHOICES	
Everyday	**Precise**
clear	evident
problem	issue, concern
show	reveal, indicate
says	notes, states

_____

(title of research paper)

Introduction

▶ **Write your introductory statement.**

Life during the Harlem Renaissance _____

_____

_____

▶ **Write your thesis statement.**

_____

_____

_____

▶ **Type your introduction on the computer or write it on paper. Then use these transition words and phrases to complete a draft of your research paper.**

Body

For example, . . .	Statistics show . . .
First of all, . . .	According to . . .
Another reason why . . .	Even though . . .
Most importantly, . . .	Finally, . . .
Similar to the . . .	In addition, . . .

Conclusion

In conclusion, . . .	It is evident that . . .
In summary, . . .	Based on my research, . . .

Revise Your Research Paper

▶ **Evaluate: Rate your research paper. Then have a writing partner rate it.**

Scoring Guide			
needs improvement	average	good	excellent
1	2	3	4

1. **UNDERLINE** the introductory statement. Does it state the research topic?

   Self   1   2   3   4
   Partner   1   2   3   4

2. **BOX** the thesis statement. Does it state what the writer will explain?

   Self   1   2   3   4
   Partner   1   2   3   4

3. **UNDERLINE** the topic sentences. Are they clear?

   Self   1   2   3   4
   Partner   1   2   3   4

4. **BOX** the controlling idea in each topic sentence. Does it make a point about the topic?

   Self   1   2   3   4
   Partner   1   2   3   4

5. ✔**CHECK** the facts and evidence. Do they support the thesis?

   Self   1   2   3   4
   Partner   1   2   3   4

6. **CIRCLE** the citations. Do they include the authors' names and page numbers in parentheses?

   Self   1   2   3   4
   Partner   1   2   3   4

7. ★**STAR** the conclusion. Does it sum up the writer's ideas about the research topic?

   Self   1   2   3   4
   Partner   1   2   3   4

▶ **Discuss: Give feedback on your partner's research paper.**

1. Start with positive comments about your partner's research paper.

   A strong part of your research paper is

   _____

   I enjoyed reading the section in which

   you _____

   _____

2. Give your partner suggestions for revision.

   I have a question about _____

   _____

   Your controlling ideas would be clearer if

   you _____

   _____

   Your research paper needs _____

   _____

3. Answer any questions your partner has about your suggestions.

4. Ask your partner for feedback. Use the frames below to summarize your partner's feedback.

   A strong part of my paper was . . .
   You enjoyed the section in which . . .
   You had a question about . . .
   My research paper needs . . .

▶ **Revise Now revise your research paper.**

Grammar USING ADJECTIVES THAT COMPARE

An **adjective** is a word that tells about or describes a noun. Adjectives can compare two or more people, places, or things.

- To use an adjective to **compare two things**, add -*er* to the adjective or use the word *more*.
- To use an adjective to **compare three or more things**, add -*est* to the adjective or use the word *most*.

Example

Adjective Comparing Two Things	Adjective Comparing Three or More Things
My father was **angrier** than Mama.	He was the **angriest** person in our house.
I was more **daring** than my friend Clyde.	I was the **most daring** kid in Harlem.

▶ **Circle the correct comparing word in the sentences below.**

1. Harlem is [quieter quietest] now than it was during the 1930s.

2. Walter was the [luckier luckiest] boy in the neighborhood.

3. Crazy Johnny helped [more most] people than the other residents.

4. The Harlem Globetrotters became the [more most] inspiring team in the city.

5. Langston Hughes was the [more famous most famous] writer to live in Harlem.

6. His poems are [shorter shortest] than the other writers' poems.

▶ **Rewrite the sentences to compare three or more things correctly.**

7. The Apollo Theater was the <u>more</u> exciting place in New York City.

_____

8. Walter was the <u>tougher</u> boy on the block.

_____

9. Mama was the <u>more</u> forgiving person in our family.

_____

10. Hurting Mama's feelings caused me the <u>more</u> agony.

_____

▶ **Edit Your Draft.** Take a close look at each sentence in your draft. **Are the adjectives that compare correct?** Fix the ones that are not.

Usage CORRECTING SENTENCE FRAGMENTS

Each **sentence** must state a complete idea.

- You can often add a subject or a verb to a sentence fragment to form a complete sentence.

Example

Correct	Incorrect
Harlem is a great place to grow up!	A great place to grow up!
Harlem was home to many famous writers, such as Langston Hughes.	Such as Langston Hughes.

▶ **Find and correct five errors in this paragraph.**

Student Model

According to Myers's memoir. Harlem was an interesting neighborhood. It was filled with several charecters who behaved strangely. The more stranger was Crazy Johnny. He didn't have any friends, but he was like a big brother. Like in my neighborhood. We have Singing Joe. Nobody knows his backround, but he always tries to help people. When he walks around the neighborhood, he sings old songs. No one ever laughs at him because we know he's a good person.

CHECK AND CORRECT

- ☐ Correct two sentence fragments.
- ☐ **UNDERLINE** one error with a comparison.
- ☐ CIRCLE two spelling errors and correct them.

▶ **Edit Your Draft.** Look at each sentence in your draft. **Does each one contain a subject and a verb?** Fix the ones that do not.

Final Draft/Present

▶ **Write a final draft of your research paper on the computer or on paper. Check it again and correct any errors before you present it.**

Focus Skill Analyze Information

Analyze Song Lyrics

Lyrics are the words of a song. These lyrics were written by Irving Mills and the music was written by Duke Ellington. Ellington was a famous jazz musician during the Harlem Renaissance.

▶ **Read the song lyrics below. Then answer the questions.**

> **MARK IT**
> - **UNDERLINE** the words that rhyme.
> - (CIRCLE) the lines that repeat. This is called the refrain, or chorus.
> - ★**STAR** when the song was written.

It Don't Mean A Thing (If It Ain't Got That Swing)

Music by Duke Ellington, 1931
Lyrics by Irving Mills

What good is melody, what good is music

If it ain't possessin' something sweet

It ain't the melody, it ain't the music

There's something else that makes the tune complete

It don't mean a thing, if it ain't got that swing

It don't mean a thing, all you got to do is sing

It makes no diff'rence if it's sweet or hot

Just give that rhythm ev'rything you got

It don't mean a thing, if it ain't got that swing

❶ **According to Ellington, what makes music complete?**

Ⓐ the melody

Ⓑ the musician

Ⓒ the swing

Ⓓ the instrument

❷ **Based on what you know about life during the Harlem Renaissance, how do you think this song sounds when it is played?**

Ⓐ slow, played with only one instrument

Ⓑ slow, played with several instruments

Ⓒ fast, played with only one instrument

Ⓓ fast, played with several instruments

❸ ✔**CHECK What do you think "swing" means in this song?**

❑ waving a golf club

❑ playing in the park

❑ making something special

❑ dancing with a partner

❹ **What do you think the song is saying?**

I think this song is saying _____

_____

_____

_____

_____

Jazz Musician
Christian McBride

This internationally famous bass player loves to make music.

▶ **Read the interview and job information. Then answer the questions below about Christian McBride's job.**

S **Scholastic: What makes Harlem special for musicians today?**

Christian McBride: There's a lot of diversity and energy here. Harlem allows me to play a broad range of music—gospel, jazz, and Latin. Through my work at the National Jazz Museum, I try to share the history of jazz with visitors.

S **Did you have a mentor who helped you in your career?**

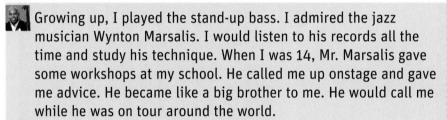

Growing up, I played the stand-up bass. I admired the jazz musician Wynton Marsalis. I would listen to his records all the time and study his technique. When I was 14, Mr. Marsalis gave some workshops at my school. He called me up onstage and gave me advice. He became like a big brother to me. He would call me while he was on tour around the world.

S **Do you mentor younger musicians now?**

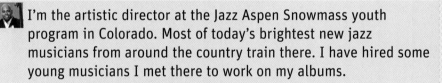

I'm the artistic director at the Jazz Aspen Snowmass youth program in Colorado. Most of today's brightest new jazz musicians from around the country train there. I have hired some young musicians I met there to work on my albums.

1 **What information must Christian McBride analyze in his career as a musician and artistic director?**

_____

_____

2 **How interesting do you think McBride's job is? Mark the line.**

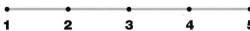

1   **2**   **3**   **4**   **5**

Not very interesting   Very interesting

3 **I would/wouldn't want** (circle one) **McBride's job because**

_____

_____

ON THE JOB

LOCATION

New York, New York

EDUCATION

High school degree; one year at the Juilliard School for Music

RESPONSIBILITIES

- Composes, records, and performs music
- Works with recording companies and agents
- Teaches jazz music and history

SKILLS

- Reading and writing music
- Playing musical instruments
- Collaborating on music projects with other musicians

SALARY

$50,000 and up

WHY MENTORS MATTER

"My mentor helped me succeed every step of the way."

CAREER CONNECTION

Arts, A/V Technology, and Communication
www.careerclusters.org

Related Jobs
- recording agent
- music teacher
- band manager

Focus Skills | Think Creatively | Present Effectively

Write a song about Harlem.

Your team has been asked to contribute to an album that honors Harlem today. Write the lyrics to a song **to include on this album.**

❶ **Take notes.** Review the readings in Workshop 9. From each reading, list descriptive words and phrases that describe Harlem.

Reading 1: "Heartbeat of Harlem"

• *artistic* _____

• _____

• _____

Reading 2: *Bad Boy*

• *busy streets in big city* _____

• _____

• _____

Reading 3: "Langston Hughes's Harlem"

• *Neon lights* _____

• _____

• _____

❷ **Collaborate.** Think about the theme, or message, of the song you will write. What will you say about Harlem? Use this web to brainstorm ideas.

The energy of Harlem will last forever.

Theme

3 **Write your lyrics.** Use your theme to brainstorm a song title. Then, plan with your group how you will present your song.

The verse is a section of the song, in the same way as a stanza is a section of a poem.

_____
(song title)

By _____
(names of members of your group)

First Verse

_____

_____

The chorus states your main theme—it is repeated after every verse.

_____

_____

Chorus or Refrain

_____

_____

_____

Second Verse

Try to have your song lyrics tell a story, or show different parts of your theme.

_____

_____

_____

_____

Chorus or Refrain

_____

_____

_____

Comprehension

▶ **Fill in the circle next to the correct answer.**

1. Who were the Harlem Globetrotters?
- Ⓐ a basketball team
- Ⓑ a group of jazz musicians
- Ⓒ a group of artists and writers
- Ⓓ people who moved to Harlem from the South

Here's a Tip.
Check your work against the reading you're being tested on. Make sure your answer agrees with what's in the reading.

2. In "Bad Boy," what was Walter's main problem?
- Ⓐ He was the new kid in school.
- Ⓑ He got hurt and lied about it.
- Ⓒ His neighborhood was getting crowded.
- Ⓓ His family was moving away.

CRITICAL READING

3. Evaluate: What was the most likely reason Langston Hughes wrote poems about dreams?
- Ⓐ to help people who have trouble sleeping
- Ⓑ to show that people in cities have positive feelings about nature
- Ⓒ to show how harsh weather affects people's lives
- Ⓓ to inspire people to follow their dreams

4. Based on this Workshop, which of the following statements about the Harlem Renaissance is true?
- Ⓐ Nobody wanted to live in Harlem.
- Ⓑ People were not encouraged to use their talents.
- Ⓒ There was a lot of violence in Harlem.
- Ⓓ It was an exciting, creative time in Harlem's history.

CRITICAL READING

5. Analyze: Which of the following texts would not belong in this Workshop?
- Ⓐ a feature story about the Harlem Globetrotters
- Ⓑ a science blog post about nightmares
- Ⓒ a short story about a girl in Harlem
- Ⓓ a profile of poet Langston Hughes

Vocabulary

▶ **Fill in the circle next to the correct definition of the underlined word.**

1. Being dragged by a cab is an <u>incident</u> that Walter Dean Myers never forgot.

   Ⓐ story

   Ⓑ joke

   Ⓒ dream

   Ⓓ event

2. Walter Dean Myers was in <u>agony</u> from his cuts and bruises.

   Ⓐ pain

   Ⓑ loneliness

   Ⓒ trouble

   Ⓓ laughter

3. He didn't want to answer his father's <u>inquiry</u> about how he got hurt.

   Ⓐ complaint

   Ⓑ question

   Ⓒ lie

   Ⓓ answer

▶ **Choose the correct definition for the underlined multiple-meaning word.**

4. Walter's injuries were <u>minor</u>. They could have been a lot worse.

   Ⓐ under the age of eighteen

   Ⓑ a subject that you study

   Ⓒ less serious

   Ⓓ major

▶ **Choose the correct word to complete the sentence.**

5. Walter's _____ answer to everything was "Nothing."

   Ⓐ unicycle

   Ⓑ universe

   Ⓒ universal

   Ⓓ university

Short Answer

CRITICAL READING ▶ **Synthesize:** Use what you've read in this Workshop to answer the question below. Check your spelling and grammar.

Describe Harlem, giving at least two details from the readings.

_____

_____

_____

_____

_____

GLOSSARY

A glossary is a useful tool found at the back of many books. It contains information about key words in the text. Look at the sample glossary entry below.

This is an entry word— the word you look up. It is divided into syllables.

The pronunciation guide appears after the entry word. Letters and letter combinations stand for different sounds. The accented syllable is marked in boldfaced letters.

This tells you what part of speech the entry word is.

cy•cle (**sye**-kuhl)

1. *noun* A sequence of events that repeats itself. *The seasons follow the same cycle every year.*
2. *verb* To ride a bicycle. *I like to cycle in the park with my friends.*

A number appears at the beginning of each meaning when more than one meaning is given for the entry word.

The meaning or meanings for the entry word appear here.

cycle

a•ban•don
(uh-**ban**-duhn) *verb*
To leave behind. *The sailors had to abandon the ship when it sank.*

ag•i•ta•tion
(aj-uh-**tay**-shuhn) *noun*
Anxiety, nervousness, or worry. *Extreme agitation prevented me from doing well in the track meet.*

ag•o•ny
(**ag**-uh-nee) *noun*
Great pain or suffering. *Rashawn screamed in agony when he broke his arm.*

al•ter
(**awl**-tur) *verb*
To change in some way. *The builder altered the house by adding a front porch.*

anx•i•e•ty
(ang-**zye**-uh-tee) *noun*
A strong feeling of worry. *The thought of another test filled Theresa with anxiety.*

ap•pre•ci•ate
(uh-**pree**-shee-ate) *verb*
To like and feel grateful for something. *I appreciate your kindness.*

ap•prox•i•mate•ly
(uh-**prok**-si-muht-lee) *adverb*
Figured out by guess or estimate, but nearly correct. *We need approximately two days to finish the project.*

as•sist
(uh-**sisst**)
1. *verb* To help. *I like to assist my mom with dinner.*
2. *noun* A play or pass that helps a teammate score. *Freddy made two assists in the championship game.*

as•sure
(uh-**shur**) *verb*
To promise. *I assure you that I will be at the party on time.*

at•ti•tude
(**at**-i-tood) *noun*
1. An opinion or feeling about something. *Alicia has a positive attitude about her work.*
2. *(slang)* A bossy or stuck-up manner. *Once she became famous, she developed an attitude.*

au•thor•i•ty
(uh-**thor**-uh-tee) *noun*
Someone who knows a lot about something. *The zoologist is an authority on polar bears.*

ben•e•fit
(**ben**-uh-fit) *noun*
1. A good result. *Good health is a benefit of eating well.*
2. An event held to raise money for a cause. *We held a benefit for our school band.*

bi•zarre
(bi-**zar**) *adjective*
Very strange. *His hairstyle was bizarre, with five colors and six different lengths of hair.*

bond
(**bond**)
1. *noun* A feeling of connection between people or groups. *My brother and I are twins, so we have a strong bond.*
2. *verb* To stick together. *You can use glue to bond the pieces of your model airplane.*

border

bor•der
(**bor**-dur) *noun*
The line that divides two countries. *The border between the U.S. and Mexico is southwest of here.*

ca•pa•ble
(**kay**-puh-buhl) *adjective*
Able to do something. *My younger sister is capable of taking care of herself.*

Prefixes

Incapable begins with the prefix *in-*, meaning "not." A **prefix** is a letter or group of letters added to the beginning of a word. A prefix changes the meaning of a word. *Incapable* means "not able to do something."

climate

cli•mate
(**klye**-mit) *noun*
Weather conditions. *The climate where seals live is usually very cold.*

com•mu•ni•cate
(kuh-**myoo**-nuh-kate) *verb*
To share information. *Sam prefers to communicate by phone.*

con•fi•dence
(**kon**-fuh-denss) *noun*
Belief in one's ability to do well. *The coach's pep talk gave our team the confidence we needed to win the tournament.*

con•spic•u•ous
(khun-**spik**-yoo-uhss) *adjective*
Very easy to notice. *Her absence from the party was conspicuous.*

con•stant
(**kon**-stuhnt) *adjective*
Nonstop; all the time. *My clock makes a constant ticking noise.*

con•vert
(kuhn-**vurt**) *verb*
To make into something else. *Dad wants to convert our basement into a guest room.*

con•vince
(kuhn-**vinss**) *verb*
To make someone believe or do something. *I had to convince my parents to let me stay out late.*

cur•rent•ly
(**kur**-uhnt-lee) *adverb*
At the present time. *My mom currently works at the mall.*

cy•cle
(**sye**-kuhl)
1. *noun* A sequence of events that repeats itself. *The seasons follow the same cycle every year.*
2. *verb* To ride a bicycle. *I like to cycle in the park with my friends.*

Compound Words

Motorcycle is a compound word. A **compound word** is made up of two smaller words, like *motor+cycle*.

de•ceive
(di-**seev**) *verb*
To trick. *My brother tried to deceive me by changing his voice on the phone.*

de•fer
(di-**fur**) *verb*
To delay. *We had to defer our trip by a week due to bad weather.*

de•gree
(di-**gree**) *noun*
1. A unit of measurement. *The temperature went up five degrees this afternoon.*
2. A title given by a college or university, such as a degree in medicine or law. *Diane received her law degree from the University of Texas.*

de•pend•ent
(di-**pen**-duhnt) *adjective*
Needing help. *When I broke my ankle, I was dependent on my family and friends.*

de•port
(di-**port**) *verb*
To send someone back to his or her original country. *The U.S. never deports immigrants for not speaking English.*

de•press•ing
(di-**press**-ing) *adjective*
Making you feel sad. *A dark, rainy day can be depressing.*

de•prive
(di-**prive**) *verb*
To hold back something that is needed or wanted. *No one should deprive a dog of food or water.*

de•spair
(di-**spair**) noun
A feeling of being very unhappy and having no hope. *After Lisa's parents died, she was full of despair.*

de•struc•tion
(di-**struhk**-shuhn) noun
Terrible damage. *The storm caused destruction all over town.*

destruction

dra•mat•ic
(druh-**mat**-ik) adjective
Very large or exciting. *Ivan wanted a dramatic change in his looks, so he dyed his hair.*

e•con•o•my
(i-**kon**-uh-mee) noun
The way products and services are created, bought, and sold. *When the economy is bad, people often lose their jobs.*

en•vi•ron•ment
(en-**vye**-ruhn-muhnt) noun
Surroundings or habitat. *I like to do my homework in a quiet environment.*

er•ror
(**er**-ur) noun
A mistake. *Tina made only one error on the test.*

e•vac•u•ate
(i-**vak**-yoo-ate) verb
To leave due to an emergency. *We had to evacuate because of the flood.*

evacuate

ev•i•dent
(**ev**-uh-duhnt) adjective
Easily noticed or understood. *It is evident that you don't believe what I'm saying.*

ex•ceed
(ek-**seed**) verb
To be greater than a particular number or amount. *If you exceed the speed limit, you may get a ticket.*

ex•cel
(ek-**sel**) verb
To do something extremely well. *I practice every day, so I excel at playing basketball.*

ex•cru•ci•a•ting
(ek-**skroo**-shee-ay-ting) adjective
Extremely painful. *The pain from this cavity is excruciating.*

ex•haust
(eg-**zawst**) verb
To tire out completely. *A marathon can exhaust even a great runner.*

ex•pand
(ek-**spand**) verb
1. To get bigger. *The balloon will expand when you fill it with air.*
2. To add more to something you have already said. *I will expand on my idea in a speech.*

fo•cus
(**foh**-kuhss) verb
1. To pay close attention. *Please focus on these directions.*
2. To adjust a camera lens so that it takes a clear, sharp image. *I focus my lens on the flower and then take a picture.*

gen•er•a•tion
(jen-uh-**ray**-shuhn) noun
All the people of about the same age in a family. *People in our generation can surf the Internet easily.*

gen•u•ine•ly
(**jen**-yoo-uhn-lee) adverb
Truly or sincerely. *I genuinely believe she's telling the truth.*

har•ass
(huh-**rass**) verb
To pick on or make fun of. *My older brother likes to harass me and my friends.*

i•den•ti•ty
(eye-**den**-ti-tee) noun
Who a person is. *I had to show proof of my identity before boarding the plane.*

im•mi•grant
(**im**-uh-gruhnt) *noun*
A person who moves from one country to another. *My grandfather was an immigrant from Mexico.*

im•pact
(**im**-pakt) *noun*
The effect an event has on someone or something. *Opening the store an hour early had a huge impact on sales that day.*

im•pos•tor
(im-**poss**-tur) *noun*
Someone who pretends to be someone else. *An Elvis look-alike is an impostor.*

im•press
(im-**press**) *verb*
To make someone admire something. *I hope to impress my boss by working extra hard.*

in•ci•dent
(**in**-suh-duhnt) *noun*
An event. *The mall was shut down after an incident involving teen violence.*

in•come
(**in**-kuhm) *noun*
Money from a job. *I worked more hours this year, so my income was higher.*

in•crease
(in-**kreess**) *verb*
To make or get larger. *To increase the size of her muscles, Ashley lifts weights every day.*

in•flu•ence
(**in**-floo-uhnss) *verb*
To change or affect something. *The job market will probably influence your career plans.*

i•ni•ti•ate
(i-**nish**-ee-ate) *verb*
To start something. *My goal this school year is to initiate a new friendship with someone.*

Synonyms

To *initiate* is "to start something" and to *commence* is "to begin or start something." These words are *synonyms*, words that have similar meanings.

in•quir•y
(in-**kwye**-ree) *noun*
A question. *I made an inquiry to the store owner about how to return a damaged shirt.*

in•struct
(in-**struhkt**) *verb*
To teach or direct. *The coach will instruct the team on how to pass the ball.*

instruct

in•tense
(in-**tenss**) *adjective*
Very extreme or having a strong effect. *The intense fire was strong enough to heat the whole house.*

in•ter•fere
(in-tur-**fihr**) *verb*
To get into or do things in a situation where you are not wanted or needed. *My friends often interfere when they think I'm making a mistake.*

in•ter•na•tion•al
(in-tur-**nash**-uh-nuhl) *adjective*
Relating to one or more countries. *The United Nations is an international organization.*

international

in•vade
(in-**vade**) *verb*
To move into a place and cause harm. *The soldiers tried to invade the fort.*

in•volved
(in-**volvd**) *adjective*
Included in a group, activity, or event. *My friends and I are involved in planning a party.*

i•so•lat•ed

(**eye**-suh-late-id) *adjective*
1. All alone. *I feel isolated whenever my best friend is absent from school.*
2. Far away from other things. *The island was isolated from the mainland by 1,000 miles of ocean.*

la•bor

(**lay**-bur) *noun*
Hard work. *Child labor is an issue in many countries.*

labor

lin•ger

(**ling**-gur) *verb*
To wait around. *Lydia will linger by the concert stage door until her favorite singer finally comes out.*

lux•u•ry

(**luhk**-zhuh-ree) *noun*
Something very rich and special. *Christopher loved luxury, so he saved up to buy himself fancy designer shirts.*

ma•jor

(**may**-jur)
1. *adjective* Very large or important. *I need to study all weekend for a major test on Monday!*
2. *noun* The main subject one studies at college. *My major in college is communications.*

man•age

(**man**-ij) *verb*
To be able to do something that is difficult. *With proper training, I know I can manage to run a marathon.*

man•u•al

(**man**-yoo-uhl)
1. *adjective* By hand. *It was hard work to get water from the manual pump.*
2. *noun* A set of instructions that tell how to use something. *I had to read the manual to learn how to use my new phone.*

mel•an•cho•ly

(**mel**-uhn-kol-ee) *adjective*
Sorrowful. *My friends told silly jokes to get me out of my melancholy mood.*

men•tal

(**men**-tuhl) *adjective*
Having to do with the mind. *Getting ready for a test takes a lot of mental energy.*

men•tor

(**men**-tor) *noun*
Someone who offers help and guidance. *My mentor helped me learn how to succeed at my first job.*

me•tal•lic

(muh-**tal**-ik) *adjective*
Made of metal. *My sister likes to wear metallic jewelry.*

meth•od
(**meth**-uhd) *noun*
A way of doing something.
*One method of getting a stain
out is to pour vinegar on it.*

min•i•mum
(**min**-uh-muhm) *adjective*
The least or smallest amount.
*Mom got angry when I did only
the bare minimum to help her.*

mi•nor
(**mye**-nur)
1. *adjective* Less important or
less serious. *Joe had a minor
cut, so he didn't go to the doctor.*
2. *noun* Someone under the
age of eighteen. *Minors are not
allowed to vote in elections.*

Homophones

Minor means "less
important" and *miner*
means "a person who digs
for coal or other minerals."
These are *homophones*,
words that sound alike but
have different spellings and
meanings.

mi•nor•i•ty
(muh-**nor**-uh-tee) *noun*
A group that is less than half
of the whole population. *Most
of us like pizza, but a minority
of us do not.*

moist
(**moist**) *adjective*
Damp. *Please wipe the table
with a moist cloth.*

mon•i•tor
(**mon**-uh-tur)
1. *verb* To track or follow.
*My coach wants to monitor my
progress for the next two years.*
2. *noun* A piece of equipment
that shows information on a
screen. *Graphic artists work on
large computer monitors.*

monitor

mo•ti•vate
(**moh**-tuh-vate) *verb*
To make someone want to do
something. *Our coach motivates
us by giving pep talks.*

mul•ti•ply
(**muhl**-tuh-plye) *verb*
To grow in number rapidly. *I
want to kill all the weeds before
they multiply.*

na•tive
(**nay**-tiv) *noun*
Originally from an area. *My
best friend is a native of Ohio.*

neg•a•tive
(**neg**-uh-tiv) *adjective*
1. Bad, harmful. *His father's
arrest had a negative effect on
Peter.*
2. Giving the answer "no." *I
asked Jaden if he wanted to go
to the movies, but his reply was
negative.*

op•tion
(**op**-shuhn) *noun*
A choice. *The teacher gave
us more than one option for
our project.*

Noun Endings

To make a noun plural,
most nouns just need an *s*,
like **options**. But nouns
that already end in an *s*
need *–es*, like *buses.*
Nouns that end in *y* need
–ies, like *policies.*

par•ti•ci•pate
(par-**tiss**-uh-pate) *verb*
To be part of something. *I
participate in as many after-
school activities as possible.*

pe•cu•liar
(pi-**kyoo**-lyur) *adjective*
Strange. *Sometimes I hear
peculiar noises at our cabin.*

per•cent
(pur-**sent**) *noun*
A part of the whole. *Eighty
percent of the students went to
the dance.*

perch
(**purch**) *noun*
A high place. *My windowsill is
that bird's favorite perch.*

per•sist
(pur-**sist**) *verb*
To continue doing something,
even though it is difficult. *I
will persist in searching for a
job until I find one.*

pes•ti•cide
(**pess**-tuh-side) *noun*
A chemical used to kill pests, such as insects that destroy crops. *Some farmers spray pesticides to prevent their crops from being destroyed.*

phe•nom•e•non
(fe-**nom**-uh-non) *noun*
An event of scientific interest. *The astronomer studied the phenomenon of the comet that appeared every eighty years.*

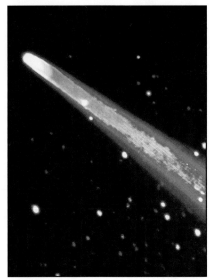
phenomenon

pit•y
(**pit**-ee) *verb*
To feel sorry for someone. *I pity anyone who has to play softball against our team!*

poi•son•ous
(**poi**-zuhn-uhss) *adjective*
Containing a substance that can cause illness or death. *Don't eat wild berries because they may be poisonous.*

pol•i•cy
(**pol**-uh-see) *noun*
A rule. *Our school has a policy against bringing pets to class.*

pos•i•tive
(**poz**-uh-tiv) *adjective*
1. Very sure that something is right or true. *Joe is positive that he will win the next game.*
2. Hopeful and confident, focused on what is good in a situation. *I want to stay positive about the role I got in the play.*

pre•cise•ly
(pri-**sisse**-lee) *adverb*
Exactly. *We left for the airport at precisely 4:15 pm.*

pres•sure
(**presh**-ur) *noun*
A force or a stressful demand. *The clerk was under heavy pressure to make more sales.*

pre•vent
(pri-**vent**) *verb*
To stop from happening. *Brushing your teeth will help to prevent tooth decay.*

> ## Antonyms
> **Prevent** means "to stop something from happening" and **permit** means "to allow something to happen." These words are **antonyms**, words that have opposite meanings.

prin•ci•ple
(**prin**-suh-puhl) *noun*
A basic truth or belief. *The principle of equality is very important in our school.*

pro•duce
1. (pruh-**dooss**) *verb* To make something. *They produce cars at that factory.*
2. (**prod**-ooss) *noun* Food that has been grown or farmed, such as fruits and vegetables. *I think fresh produce tastes better than canned vegetables.*

pur•pose
(**pur**-puhss) *noun*
A reason for doing something. *My purpose for mowing lawns is to earn some money.*

quiv•er
(**kwiv**-ur)
1. *verb* To shake. *A cold chill ran down my spine, and I began to quiver.*
2. *noun* A case for holding arrows. *He carried his arrows to the archery tournament in a new quiver.*

> ## Multiple-Meaning Words
> *Quiver* means "to shake." It also means "a case for holding arrows." **Multiple-meaning words** are words that have more than one meaning.

re•bel
1. (ri-**bel**) *verb* To act out against someone in a position of power. *Some teenagers feel the need to rebel against their parents.*
2. (**reb**-ul) *noun* Someone who fights against a government or the people in charge of something. *The rebels closed in on the army headquarters.*

rebel

rec•og•nize
(**rek**-uhg-nize) *verb* To see or hear someone and know who the person is. *My friends did not recognize me with my new haircut.*

rec•om•mend
(rek-uh-**mend**) *verb* To suggest a certain action. *I recommend that you read this fabulous story.*

re•cov•er•y
(ri-**kuhv**-ur-ee) *noun* The process of getting back to normal. *The doctor said Tom's recovery from the accident would be quick.*

re•form
(ri-**form**) *verb* To make something better by changing it. *Some politicians want to reform tax laws.*

re•in•force
(ree-in-**forss**) *verb* To make something stronger. *We have to reinforce our skating ramp so that it will be safe to skate on.*

re•ject
1. (ri-**jekt**) *verb* To turn down. *I will reject the job offer because the job seems boring.*
2. (**ree**-jekt) *noun* Something that has been thrown away. *I chose two peaches that were still fresh and put a reject in the compost bin.*

re•lease
(ri-**leess**) *verb* To give off or let go of something. *I always release a fish right after I catch it.*

re•move
(ri-**moov**) *verb* To take something away. *Please remove your plate from the table after you finish eating.*

re•nais•sance
(**ren**-uh-sahnss) *noun* Renewal, rebirth. *Many people believe that American culture is experiencing a renaissance.*

re•quire
(ri-**kwire**) *verb* To need something. *Most restaurants require customers to wear shoes.*

re•side
(ri-**zide**) *verb* To live in a particular place. *Not many young people reside in my building.*

res•i•dent
(**rez**-uh-duhnt) *noun* Someone who lives in a particular place. *The residents like to sit in front of their house.*

residents

res•o•lute
(**rez**-uh-loot) *adjective* Feeling strong and certain about something. *José argued with his parents, but they were resolute in their decision that he could not come to my party.*

re•sourc•es
(ri-**sorss**-ez) *noun* Supplies that you need to do something. *The library has many great resources for research papers.*

re•spond
(ri-**spond**) *verb* To react to something that has been said or done. *I need to respond to my aunt's invitation.*

re•spon•si•ble
(ri-**spon**-suh-buhl) *adjective* Being the cause of or the reason for something. *My sister claims I am responsible for every mess.*

re•verse
(ri-**vurss**)
1. *verb* To change to the opposite position. *Tina reversed her opinion of the band when she heard their great new album.*
2. *verb* To turn something around, upside down, or inside out. *I got a stain on my shirt, so I reversed it and wore it inside out.*
3. *noun* The control in a vehicle that makes it go backward. *He put the forklift in reverse to back up.*

reverse

sac•ri•fice
(**sak**-ruh-fisse) *verb*
To give up. *I had to sacrifice my plans to help my brother with his homework.*

se•cure
(si-**kyoor**) *adjective*
Safe and not likely to be at risk. *The movie star felt secure when his bodyguard was nearby.*

se•vere
(suh-**veer**) *adjective*
Very bad or serious. *Happily, Ric survived a severe car crash.*

somb•rous
(**somb**-ruhss) *adjective*
Gloomy and depressing. *Madeline's funeral took place on a cloudy and sombrous day.*

spe•cies
(**spee**-sheez) *noun*
One of the groups into which plants and animals are divided. *The lion and the cheetah are two different species of cat.*

sur•geon
(**sur**-juhn) *noun*
A doctor who performs operations. *My uncle studied medicine; now, he's a surgeon.*

sus•tain
(suh-**stayn**) *verb*
1. To suffer something. *My dog fell out a window, but he didn't sustain any injuries.*
2. To keep something going. *I can sustain a handstand for 11 minutes.*

Verb Endings

The past-tense form of *sustain* is *sustained*. The present-tense form is *sustain*. **Verb endings** show when an action takes place. To show an action in the past, you often can add *–ed*. If a verb ends with the letter e, it is usually dropped before adding *-ed* or *–ing*.

---

tense
(**tenss**) *adjective*
Nervous. *I get tense when I'm around a lot of people.*

threat•en
(**thret**-uhn) *verb*
To be likely to harm or destroy something. *The storm's heavy wind threatened the trees on the island.*

tone
(**tohn**) *noun*
A way of speaking that shows a certain feeling. *My dad's voice changes tone when he is angry.*

trend
(**trend**) *noun*
A pattern of change over time. *Some fashion trends repeat every few years.*

u•nique
(yoo-**neek**) *adjective*
Special and one-of-a-kind. *My best friend gave me a unique handmade necklace.*

u•ni•ver•sal
(yoo-nuh-**vur**-suhl) *adjective*
Concerning all the members of a group or of the world. *It's a universal agreement at our school that the walls need to be painted.*

ut•ter
(**uht**-ur)
1. *verb* To speak or make a sound from your mouth. *I was so angry at Brian that I couldn't even utter his name.*
2. *adjective* Complete or total. *The movie was an utter disaster and a waste of time.*

va•cant
(**vay**-kuhnt) *adjective*
Empty. *They will build a stadium on the vacant lot.*

vault
(**vawlt**)
1. *noun* An underground chamber. *The queen was buried in a stone vault.*
2. *verb* To leap over something using your hands or a pole. *He can vault over a ten-foot bar.*

How to Use the Reading Handbook

This handbook includes the comprehension skills that you mastered in the *rBook*. You can use these directions and charts to review what you know. You can also use them in your other classes, like social studies and science. They can help you understand a new text or story.

Main Idea and Details

The **main idea** is the most important point about a topic. **Details** are the facts that support the main idea. To find the main idea and details:

- Decide what the topic is. Find the main idea about the topic.
- Look for the details that support the main idea.

▶ Use this chart to identify a main idea and supporting details.

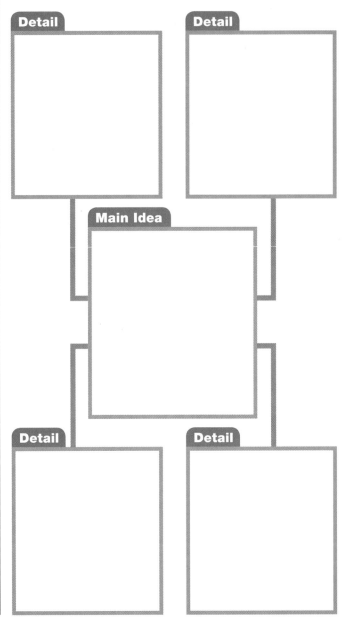

Sequence of Events

Sequence is the order in which events happen. To find the sequence of events:

- Try to remember the order in which events take place.
- Look for times, dates, and signal words, such as *first*, *then*, *next*, *after*, and *finally*.
- When you know the order, check it again. Make sure it makes sense.

▶ **Use this chart to identify a sequence of events.**

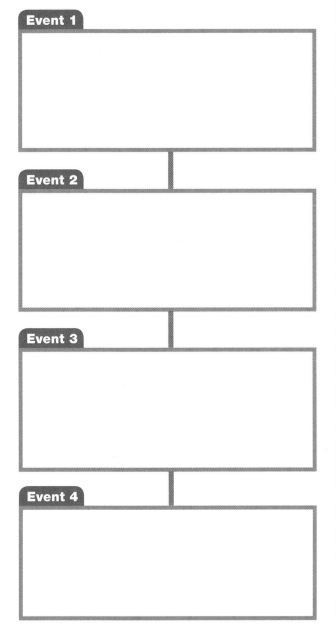

Summarize

A **summary** is a short statement of the most important ideas in a reading or part of a reading. To summarize:

- Find the topic of the text.
- Look for the most important details about the topic.
- Restate the topic and important details in a short summary. Use your own words.

▶ **Use this chart to identify the topic and important details in a text.**

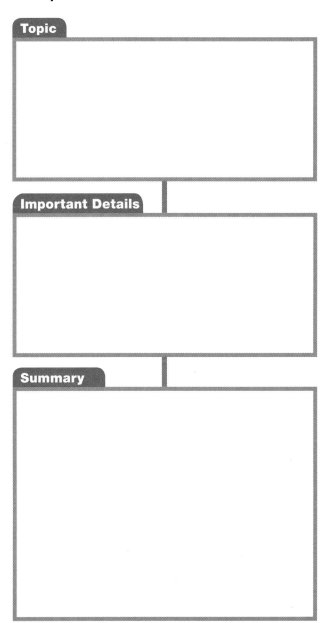

Problem and Solution

A **problem** is a situation or event that causes trouble. A **solution** is what fixes the problem. To find the problem and the solution:

- Look for signal words or phrases such as *problem*, *difficulty*, *conflict*, and *challenge*.
- Look for attempts, or ways, to solve the problem.
- Look for signal words or phrases such as *solution*, *answer*, and *results*.

▶ **Use this chart to identify a problem and a solution.**

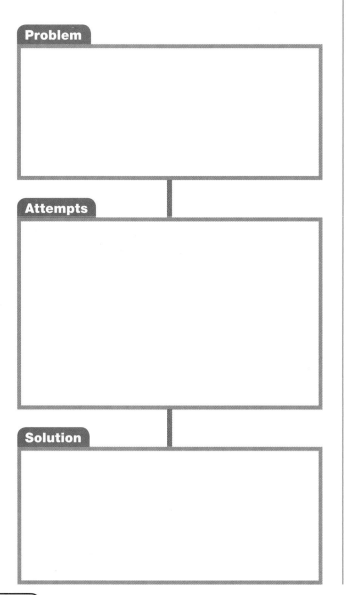

Cause and Effect

A **cause** is the reason something happens. An **effect** is the result of a cause. To find the cause and effect:

- Ask yourself "Why did it happen?" to find the cause.
- Ask yourself "What happened?" to find the effect.
- Look for signal words or phrases such as *because*, *so*, *as a result*, *therefore*, *consequently*, and *for this reason*.

▶ **Use this chart to identify cause-and-effect relationships.**

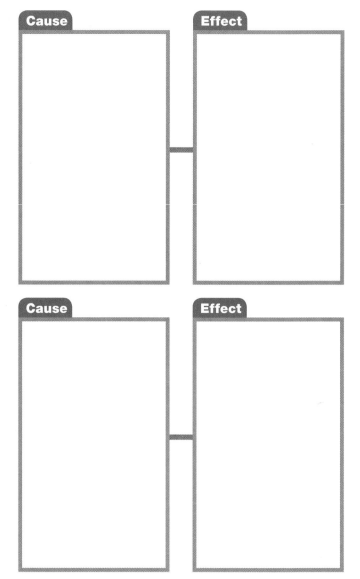

Compare and Contrast

When you **compare**, you tell how two people or things are alike. When you **contrast**, you tell how they are different. To compare and contrast:

- Ask yourself how two people or things are the same. Look for signal words and phrases such as *both*, *like*, *also*, and *in addition*.

- Ask yourself how two people or things are different. Look for signal words such as *unlike*, *but*, *rather than*, and *however*.

▶ **Use this chart to compare and contrast two elements in a reading.**

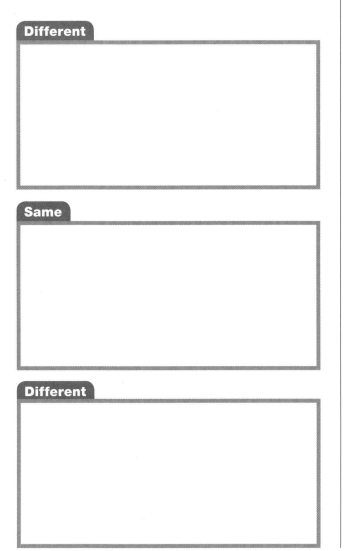

Make Inferences

When you **make inferences**, you form ideas about things that are not directly stated in the text. To make inferences:

- Look for a situation in the text in which the author gives clues but does not state exactly what is happening.

- Think about what you already know about the topic.

- Combine the text clues with your own knowledge to make an inference.

▶ **Use this chart to make an inference.**

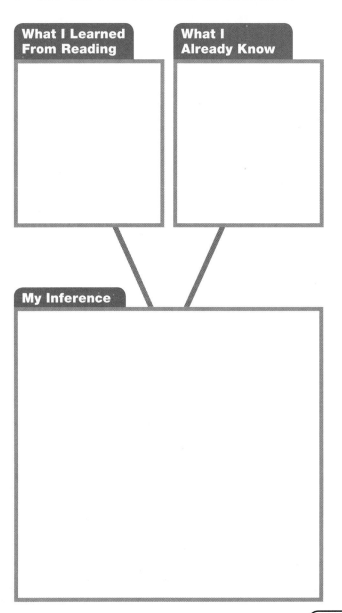

Story Elements

A short story is a brief work of fiction. It focuses on one or two main characters and on a single problem or conflict. To understand a short story, look for four elements:

Setting

Setting refers to the place and time of a story. To analyze the setting:

- Look at the illustrations.
- Look for details that tell *where*. Ask yourself, "What words in the story help me imagine what the place looks like?"
- Look for story details that tell *when* and *what time*. Ask yourself, "When does this story take place? Is it long ago, in the future, or in the present?"
- Pay attention to any changes in the setting and how they affect the story.

Character

A character is a person or animal in a story. It is who the story is about. Often, stories have several characters. The main characters are the ones the story is mostly about. Characters have special qualities, or traits, that make up their personalities. To analyze a character:

- Look for words the author uses to describe the character, especially adjectives.
- Pay attention to what the character thinks, says, and does.
- Be aware of what other characters say about the main character.
- Think about what you already know about people and their behavior.

Plot

Plot refers to what happens in a story, including the problem, the events that lead to solving the problem, and the solution. To analyze the plot:

- Find out the main character's problem.
- Look at how the character tries to solve the problem.
- Pay attention to what happens that helps solve the problem. Look at what happens that gets in the way of solving the problem.
- Think about how the story turns out. Does the character solve the problem? How?

Theme

The theme is an important message about life that the author wants readers to take away from the story. It often helps you understand the author's purpose, thoughts, and feelings. To analyze theme:

- Think about what the characters do and say.
- Think about what happens to the characters.
- Ask yourself, "What does the author want readers to know about?"

▶ **Use this chart to keep track of the setting, characters, plot, and theme of a story you are reading.**

Story Title: _____

	Part 1	Part 2	Part 3
Setting	Time: _____ _____ Places: _____ _____	Time: _____ _____ Places: _____ _____	Time: _____ _____ Places: _____ _____
Characters	Who are the main characters? _____ _____ Describe them: _____ _____	How do the characters change? _____ _____ _____ _____	What are the characters like now? _____ _____ _____ _____
Plot Events	What happens at the beginning of the story? _____ _____ _____	What happens in the middle of the story? _____ _____ _____	How does the story end? _____ _____ _____
Theme	Author's message:		

Literary Craft and Structure Terms

author a person who writes a short story, play, poem, novel, article, essay, or book

author's point of view the author's opinion of the subject he or she is writing about

bibliography a list of sources about a subject of research

biography the true account of a person's life, written by someone else

characterization the way an author tells readers about a character

characters the people or animals in a story

conflict the problem in a story. An internal conflict takes place in the mind of a character who must resolve something. An external conflict takes place between two characters or between a character and a force of nature, society, or the unknown.

dialogue a conversation between characters

essay a short piece of writing that deals with one subject

fiction an invented story about imaginary characters, events, and settings

figurative language words used to say something other than their literal meaning. Similes and metaphors use figurative language. Example: *All the world's a stage.*

flashback the return to an event that occurred before the present situation

foreshadowing hints of what is to come

genre a category, or type, of literature, such as fiction, nonfiction, poetry, and drama

historical document a speech, treaty, letter, memoir, declaration, or other important written document from the past

historical fiction a story or novel whose setting is some period in the past. Often, real people from the past or important historical events are used in works of historical fiction.

imagery the use of descriptive words and phrases to create pictures in the reader's mind. Example: *The moonlight cut through the fog and lit up the man's face.*

irony the contrast between what is expected and what actually happens

memoir a true story about the author told by him- or herself

metaphor a comparison in which something is said to be something else. Metaphors use *is* or *was*. Example: *You are a star.*

mood the general feeling that an author creates. The author often creates mood through specific description and setting.

narrator the teller of a story. A first-person narrator tells a story using the word *I.*

nonfiction a true story about real people and factual events

novel a book-length work of fiction that usually has more than one plot, character, setting, and theme

onomatopoeia the use of a word that sounds like the thing it stands for. Example: *hiss, buzz,* and *sizzle.*

personal narrative a true story about a person's life told in the first person

plot the series of events in a story, including the conflict, or problem

plot twist a turn of events in the story, novel, or play that is unexpected

poetry literature that uses language chosen for its sound and for its ability to express and evoke emotion

point of view the perspective from which a story is told. In the first-person point of view, the narrator is usually a character in the story. This narrator tells the story by using the pronouns *I* or *we*. In the third-person point of view, the narrator may or may not be a character in the story. This narrator uses the pronouns *he*, *she*, or *they*. Sometimes the narrator in the third-person point of view knows what every character is thinking and feeling. This kind of narrator is omniscient, or all-knowing.

repetition words, phrases, or sentences that are used over and over again

rhyme two or more words that have ending syllables with the same or similar sounds

rhythm a regular, repeated pattern of sounds in music or poetry

sensory details descriptive words and phrases that appeal to the reader's sense of sight, hearing, touch, smell, or taste

setting where and when a story takes place

short story a brief work of fiction

short story retelling/adaptation a brief work of fiction based on a longer work. Often, the original work is a different genre of literature, such as a play or a film script.

simile a comparison of two unlike things, using the words *like* or *as*. Example: *He was as quiet as a mouse.*

speaker/persona a character that a poet creates to tell the story in a poem. The speaker's voice is often different from the poet's voice.

stanza a group of two or more lines in a poem that are held together by length, rhyme scheme, meter, and a specific idea or topic.

suspense a state of uncertainty that keeps a reader reading

symbol something that has meaning in itself but also stands for something else. For example, in a story, a heart may also stand for love.

theme an important message about life that the author wants readers to take away from a story or poem. The author tries to help readers understand the theme by using the whole story—the title, the plot, the characters, the setting, and other literary elements such as repetition.

tone the author's attitude about the subject he or she has written about. An author's writing tone can be formal or informal.

unreliable narrator a narrator who tells a story in a way that is not completely trustworthy. An unreliable narrator may lie, distort the truth, or leave out important information as the first-person narrator while telling the story.

verse words arranged in the form of poetry

works cited a list of sources cited in a research paper

How to Use the Writing Handbook

This handbook includes the writing skills that you mastered in the *rBook*. You can use these directions and charts to review what you know. You can also use them to help you with a new writing assignment.

Informational Paragraph

An **informational paragraph** provides information and explains it.

- Identify the topic in a **topic sentence**, and include a **controlling idea** that makes your point about the topic.
- Support or explain the topic with **factual details**.
- Arrange the details in a **logical order**.
- Use **transition words and phrases** to introduce or connect the details.
- Explain why the topic is important in a **concluding sentence**.

▶ Use this chart to plan an informational paragraph.

Topic Sentence

Detail 1

Detail 2

Detail 3

Concluding Sentence

Narrative Paragraph

A **narrative paragraph** tells a story about a real or imagined event or experience.

- Identify the experience and establish a point of view in an **introductory statement**.
- Describe events in the **time order**.
- Use **sensory details** and **vivid adjectives** to bring the experience to life.
- Use **transition words and phrases** to introduce and connect details.
- Tell your feelings about the experience in a **concluding sentence**.

▶ **Use this chart to plan a narrative paragraph.**

Introductory Statement

Detail 1

Detail 2

Detail 3

Concluding Sentence

Literary Analysis Paragraph

A **literary analysis** carefully examines a text or one element of a text, such as character, plot, setting, or theme in a story.

- Identify the title, author, and text type that you will analyze in a **topic sentence**.
- Include a **controlling idea** about the text or story element.
- Use **evidence** and **direct quotations** from the text to support your analysis.
- Use **transition words and phrases** to introduce and connect details.
- Sum up your key ideas in a **concluding sentence**.

▶ **Use this chart to plan a literary analysis paragraph.**

Topic Sentence

Evidence 1

Evidence 2

Evidence 3

Concluding Sentence

Informational Summary

An **informational summary** provides an overview of the key topics and ideas from a text.

- Identify the title, author, and text type that you will summarize in an **introductory statement.**
- Include a **focus statement** that tells your plan for the essay.
- Start each body paragraph with a **topic sentence** that has a **controlling idea.**
- Use **transition words and phrases** to connect ideas and details.
- **Use your own words** in the summary, and use quotation marks for **citations** from the text.

▶ **Use this chart to plan an informational summary.**

Introduction

Body Paragraph 1

Body Paragraph 2

Body Paragraph 3

Conclusion

Argument Essay

An **argument essay** states a position or claim about an issue. Convincing evidence and reasons support the claim.

- Introduce the issue in an **introductory statement,** and present your position in a clear **thesis statement.**
- Start each body paragraph with a **topic sentence** that has a controlling idea.
- Support your position with convincing and relevant **reasons and evidence.** Point out weaknesses in an **opposing argument.**
- Use **transition words and phrases** to introduce and connect ideas.
- Offer a **recommendation** in the conclusion.

▶ **Use this chart to plan an argument essay.**

Introduction

Reason/Evidence 1

Reason/Evidence 2

Reason/Evidence 3

Conclusion

Literary Analysis Essay

A **literary analysis** carefully examines a text or one element of a text, such as character, plot, setting, or theme in a story.

- Identify the title, author, and text type that you will analyze in an **introductory statement**.
- Include a **thesis statement** that presents a plan for your essay.
- Start each body paragraph with a **topic sentence** that has a controlling idea.
- Use **evidence** and **direct quotations** from the text to support your analysis.
- Use **transition words and phrases** to introduce or connect ideas and details.
- Sum up or restate the thesis statement in the **conclusion**.

▶ **Use this chart to plan a literary analysis essay.**

Introduction

Body Paragraph 1

Body Paragraph 2

Body Paragraph 3

Conclusion

Personal Narrative

A **personal narrative** tells a story about an experience in the writer's life.

- Identify the experience and establish a point of view in an **introductory statement**.
- Describe the events in **time order**.
- Bring the story to life by including **sensory details**. Use **dialogue** to show exactly what people in the story said.
- Use **transition words and phrases** to introduce or connect ideas and details.
- Sum up the experience and its importance in the **conclusion**.

▶ **Use this chart to plan a personal narrative.**

Introduction

Body Paragraph 1

Body Paragraph 2

Body Paragraph 3

Conclusion

Research Paper

A **research paper** presents information on a subject using multiple authoritative sources.

▶ **Follow these steps before writing your research paper.**

- **Identify your writing topic.** Your teacher may assign a topic. Or, you may need to brainstorm a topic.

- **Select sources.** Gather information from reliable sources. Your sources may include books, websites, encyclopedias, magazines, and newspapers. See 21st Century Handbook: Gather Information, Evaluate Sources.

- **Research and take notes.** As you read about the topic, write down relevant facts and details. See 21st Century Handbook: Take Notes.

- **Develop a thesis statement.** Read through your notes. Then, write a thesis statement about your topic.

- **Create an outline.** Create an outline for your paper.

- **Cite your sources.** Make sure you give credit to the sources you use in your paper. Using someone else's words or ideas without giving credit is plagiarizing.

▶ **Use these tips as you write your research paper.**

- Introduce the topic in an **introductory statement**.

- Include a **thesis statement** that tells what you will explain about the topic.

- Start each body paragraph with a **topic statement** that has a **controlling idea**.

- Include **facts and evidence** that support your thesis. Use **citations** to identify your sources.

- Sum up your ideas in the **conclusion**.

▶ **Use this chart to plan a research paper.**

Introduction

Body Paragraph 1

Body Paragraph 2

Body Paragraph 3

Conclusion

Grammar

▶ IDENTIFYING SENTENCES AND FRAGMENTS

A **sentence** is a group of words that tells a complete idea.

- The subject tells who or what the sentence is about.
- The predicate tells what someone or something does.

Example

Subject	Predicate
Irene's parents	moved to America from Mexico.
My neighbors	are from China and Vietnam.

▶ CORRECTING SENTENCE FRAGMENTS

A sentence fragment is an incomplete sentence. Often, a sentence fragment is missing either a subject or a predicate. To correct some fragments, add a subject or verb to make a **complete sentence**.

Example

Sentence Fragment	Complete Sentence
A tornado our town today. [missing verb]	A tornado **struck** our town today.
Brought the trees down. [missing subject]	**A storm** brought the trees down.

To correct some sentence fragments, you can connect the fragment to a complete sentence by adding a comma and any missing words.

Example

Sentence and Fragment	Complete Sentence
A tornado struck our town today. Touched down in Texas.	A tornado struck our town today, **and then it** touched down in Texas.

▶ CORRECTING RUN-ON SENTENCES

A run-on sentence is made up of two complete thoughts that are incorrectly joined together.

- To fix a run-on sentence, separate the ideas into two **complete sentences**.
- Or, insert a comma and a connecting word between the thoughts.

Example

Run-on sentence:	Louisa lived here she ran away.
Complete sentences:	Louisa lived here. She ran away.
Complete sentence:	Louisa lived here, but she ran away.

▶ USING CORRECT VERB TENSE

The **tense** of a verb shows when the action happens.

- A **present-tense verb** shows action that is happening now.
- A past-tense verb shows action that took place in the past. Most past-tense verbs end in *-ed*.

Example

Present-Tense Verb	Past-Tense Verb
James works on a farm. James picks fruit.	James worked on a farm last summer. James picked fruit yesterday.

▶ USING IRREGULAR VERBS

Most past-tense verbs end in *-ed*. **Irregular verbs** do not.

- You must remember the different spellings of irregular past-tense verbs.
- The verb *to be* is a common irregular verb. Its **present-tense** forms are *I am*, *you are*, *he/she is*. Its past-tense forms are *I/he/she was*, *you/we/they were*.

Example

Present-Tense Verb	Past-Tense Verb
I am sorry for my actions. Amy sends out cards for birthdays. They usually eat lunch at noon.	I was sorry for my actions. She sent one to me last week. Yesterday, they ate lunch early.

▶ SUBJECT-VERB AGREEMENT

The **subject and verb** in a sentence must agree in number.

- A **singular verb** tells what one person, place, or thing is doing. It usually ends in *-s* or *-es*.
- A plural verb tells what more than one person, place, or thing is doing. It usually does not end in *-s* or *-es*.

Example

Singular Subject and Verb	Plural Subject and Verb
A noise comes from below. Usher closes the door to the vault.	The noises come from below. We close the door to the vault.

► USING SUBJECT AND OBJECT PRONOUNS

A **pronoun** is a word that takes the place of a noun in a sentence.

- Use a subject pronoun in the subject of a sentence.
- Use an object pronoun after a verb or after a word such as *for* or *to*.

Example

Subject Pronoun	Predicate Pronoun
I never liked snakes.	Snakes have always scared me.
We want to leave the island.	Snakes are too gross for us.
She found two in the house.	Our snake almost bit her.
They are just creepy.	My sister and I have them.

► USING ADJECTIVES THAT COMPARE

An **adjective** is a word that tells about or describes a noun. Adjectives can help compare two or more people, places, or things.

- To use an adjective to compare two things, add *-er* to the adjective or use the word *more*.
- To use an adjective to compare three or more things, add *-est* to the adjectives or use the word *most*.

Example

Adjective Comparing Two Things	Adjective Comparing Three or More Things
My father was angrier than Mama. I was more daring than my friend Clyde.	He is the angriest person in our house. I was the most daring kid in Harlem.

► USING ADVERBS

An **adjective** describes a person, place, or thing. An adverb describes a verb, an adjective, or another adverb. Many adverbs end in *-ly*.

- Use an adverb to make your writing more precise.

Example

Adjective	Adverb
I was patient with the new student.	I waited patiently for the new student.
Jonathan was slow at making new friends.	Jonathan made friends slowly.
We are always careful on the train.	We stepped carefully onto the train.

Usage and Mechanics

▶ USING END PUNCTUATION

Different kinds of sentences use different **end punctuation marks**.

- A **statement** always ends with a period.
- A **question** always ends with a question mark.

Example

Statement	Question
I'm from Mexico. We are a nation of immigrants.	Where are you from? Were your parents immigrants?

▶ USING CAPITAL LETTERS

Some words begin with a **capital letter**.

- The first word in a sentence begins with a capital letter.
- A proper noun begins with a capital letter.

Example

Correct	Incorrect
Lightning struck the building. The storm flooded Emily's home.	lightning struck the building. The storm flooded emily's home.

▶ USING CORRECT WORD ORDER

The **order of words** in a sentence must make sense.

- An adjective comes before the noun it describes.
- A helping verb comes just before the main verb in a statement.

Example

Correct	Incorrect
Louisa bought a new coat. I know where Louisa is going.	Louisa bought a coat new. I know where is Louisa going.

► USING COMMAS IN A SERIES

Items in a series are separated by **commas**.

- A series is a list of the same kinds of words.
- Commas follow every item in the series except the last one.

Example

Correct	Incorrect
Snakebites, cuts, and other injuries are part of the job.	Snakebites cuts and other injuries are part of the job.

► USING POSSESSIVE NOUNS

A **possessive noun** shows ownership.

- Add an apostrophe (') and an -s to a singular noun.
- Add an apostrophe to a plural noun that ends in -s.

Example

Correct	Incorrect
Poe's story scared me.	Poe story scared me.
The friends' voices were low.	The friends voices were low.

► USING COMMAS WITH INTRODUCTORY WORDS

A **comma** follows an opening word or phrase at the beginning of a sentence.

- *Yes, No, Next,* and *Later* are examples of opening words.
- *In addition* and *After a while* are examples of opening phrases.

Example

Correct	Incorrect
Next, Kim began helping others.	Next Kim began helping others.
After a while, she felt better.	After a while she felt better.

▶ AVOIDING DOUBLE NEGATIVES

Negatives are words that express *no* or *not*.

- Use only one negative word to express a single negative idea.
- It is incorrect to use two negatives to express a negative idea.

Example

Correct	Incorrect
Kudzu should never be allowed to grow near homes and schools. The brown tree snake didn't bite anyone.	Kudzu shouldn't never be allowed to grow near homes and schools. The brown tree snake didn't bite nobody.

▶ USING QUOTATION MARKS

Quotation marks show the exact words of a speaker.

- The first word of a quotation is capitalized.
- Punctuation usually goes inside the ending quotation mark.

Example

Correct	Incorrect
Lisa yelled, "Way to go!" Josue said, "You did it!"	Lisa yelled, "way to go!" Josue said, "You did it"!

▶ CORRECTING SENTENCE FRAGMENTS

Each **sentence** must state a complete idea.

- You can often add a subject or a verb to a sentence fragment to form a complete sentence.

Example

Correct	Incorrect
Harlem is a great place to grow up! Harlem was home to many famous writers, such as Langston Hughes.	A great place to grow up! Such as Langston Hughes.

How to Use the 21st Century Handbook

This handbook includes 21 skills that we all need for success in the 21st Century. These skills will help you in school, in your social life, and someday in your job or career.

Use this handbook to help you to complete the 21st Century Learning lessons and Wrap-Up Projects in the *rBook*. These skills will also be useful in other classes, like science and social studies.

Consider this set of skills your own personal toolkit for 21st Century success.

Table of Contents

Justify Arguments

Everyone has an opinion. But not everyone knows how to convince others to listen. If you want your opinion to carry weight, state your case with power.

How can I support my opinion?

▶ **Use these tips:**

- **Reasons.** Make your point by explaining clearly why you believe as you do.
- **Facts and statistics.** Numbers and facts are more convincing than words alone. Do your research, and share what you learn.
- **Examples.** Persuade others with examples that support your opinion.
- **Expert backup.** Is there an expert who believes what you do? Use that person's opinion to support your own.

Use IT!

At school: Did you love or hate a book you read? Explain why.

At home: Do you deserve a later curfew? Convince your family.

Evaluate Risk

Sometimes, taking risks is the only way to reach your goal. You might fail...but you might succeed. So take a risk, but look before you leap.

Is it a good risk to take?

▶ **Ask yourself:**

- What are the possible benefits?
- What are the possible dangers?
- Is there a better way to achieve my goal?
- What have other people done in similar situations? How has it worked out?
- Can I protect myself if I take this risk? How?

Use IT! **At school:** Should I try out for a play?

At home: Everyone else is doing it. Should I? Why or why not?

Understand Multiple Perspectives

There's more than one side to every story. To settle a complicated situation, try to understand everyone's point of view.

Can we understand each other better?

▶ **Follow these steps:**

- **Figure out what each side believes.** Restate each person's side of the story in your own words.
- **Consider why they feel that way.** What information is each person using? How is his or her attitude related to life experiences and values?
- **Evaluate what you've heard.** Which opinions and reasons do you find most convincing?
- **Decide which viewpoint you agree with, and why.** Even if you disagree with someone, at least you'll understand the person better.

Use IT! **At school:** Understand current events from more than one side.

At home: See an argument through a family member's eyes.

⚑ Make Decisions

How can you make the best choice? There's no guarantee that any decision you make will be "right." But by following the right steps, you can make the best decision possible.

How do I decide?

▶ **Follow these steps:**

- **Clearly state the decision you need to make.** What are your options?
- **Gather information.** What do you need to know about the situation and each option? Whom can you ask?
- **Weigh pros and cons.** Which option has more positives? Which will have the best outcome?
- **Make your choice.** Try not to second-guess yourself. Be confident in your choice.

Use IT! **At school:** Some of your friends have quit the track team. Should you?

At home: Should you go camping with a friend? You'll miss your mom's birthday.

★ Solve Problems

How do you face a problem? Ignore it? Sit down and put your head in your hands? There's no need to give up! With the right tools, you can solve almost any problem.

How can I solve this?

▶ **Follow these steps:**

- Collect information about the situation.
- State the problem clearly. Make sure you understand all parts of it.
- Brainstorm a few possible solutions. List the pros and the cons of each.
- Choose a solution to try. Pick the one that seems most likely to work best.
- Try out your solution. If it doesn't work, figure out why and try something else.

Use IT! **At school:** How can I go to the big game and study for the test?

At home: Your parents can't drive you. How will you get to the concert?

⑩ Set Criteria

How can you decide what passes the test? If you want to decide which movie to see or which pair of jeans to buy, be sure to first set your standards, or criteria.

What standards should I use?

▶ **Use these tips:**

- Make sure you are comparing similar items.
- Decide what qualities are most important to you.
- Make a scale, from 1 to 5, for each quality you want to compare.
- Be honest and fair when you use your criteria to make a judgment.

> **Use IT!** **At school:** Decide what will make a good source for a research project.
>
> **At home:** Compare video games to make a smart purchase.

⑦ Ask Questions

How do we get the answers we need? We ask questions! You can use different types of questions to get the information you need when you need it.

What do I ask?

▶ **Ask yourself:**

- **Recall and comprehension:** What do I need to know? What have I learned?
- **Application:** How can I use this information?
- **Analysis:** What are the parts or steps? Why does it occur?
- **Synthesis:** How can I combine what I've learned into a new idea?
- **Evaluation:** How good is it? What evidence supports it?

> **Use IT!** **At school:** What exactly is the teacher talking about?
>
> **At home:** Is that new phone worth the money?

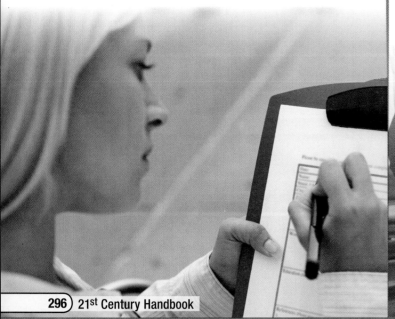

Resolve Conflicts

Conflict is a part of life. At some point, we all disagree with someone. Here's how to find a solution that feels fair to everyone involved.

How can we work this out?

▶ **Follow these steps:**

- Summarize the conflict.
- Allow each individual or group to tell their version of the story.
- Brainstorm solutions.
- Decide on a solution or course of action that everyone can agree on.
- Follow up. Make sure the solution is put into action and that everyone does what he or she should.

> **Use IT!** **At school:** Make peace during an argument between two groups.
>
> **At home:** Settle disagreements between family members.

Present Effectively

You *will* be speaking in front of a group. Whether it's an oral report in class or an update you'll give at work someday, make it a presentation they'll remember.

What's the secret of a good presentation?

▶ **Use these tips:**

- Do you need to inform, entertain, or persuade? Your purpose will affect what you present and how you present it.
- Know what you're talking about. Do the research. Get solid information.
- Use visuals. Photographs, slide shows, maps, and graphs can add interest.
- Use your eyes and voice. Look at listeners often as you speak. Speak loudly and clearly.

> **Use IT!** **At school:** Deliver a speech that will get everyone listening.
>
> **At home:** Entertain others with a slide show of a recent event.

21ST CENTURY HANDBOOK

🖥 Build an Effective Team

People need to work together. But not every team can get the job done. You need a team that can work together to accomplish goals.

How can we build a good team?

▶ **Follow these steps:**

- Clarify your goals. Brainstorm a list of tasks.
- Discuss who would be the best person for each job.
- Follow up on the work. Is everyone doing what he or she should?
- Work through problems as a team.

Use IT! **At school:** Do a complicated science experiment.

At home: Hold a group tag sale.

 Brainstorming

Think "outside the box." When you let your mind explore many possibilities, you can solve problems, gather cool and useful facts, and end up with a bunch of great ideas.

What are the possibilities?

▶ **Use these tips:**

- **Let it flow.** The purpose of brainstorming is to gather many ideas quickly. Let your mind go in many directions, and jot down ideas as they come to you.
- **Use 5 Ws and an H.** Get your mind going by asking questions that begin with *who, what, when, where, why,* and *how.*
- **Write now, judge later! Write quickly to keep the ideas flowing.** You can go back later to choose your best ideas, or to polish what you have written.

Use IT! **At school:** Come up with a theme for a group project.

At home: Figure out the perfect system for organizing your stuff.

Think Creatively

A creative mind is a force to reckon with. Creative thinking can help with almost any task. Learn how you can be more inventive.

How can I use my creativity?

▶ **Use these tips:**

- **Identify your goal.** Are you writing a play? Working on a social studies project? Trying to solve a problem? What is the outcome you're looking for?

- **Think outside the box.** Use your brainstorming skills, and don't reject new or "crazy" ideas. Ask yourself, "What's the opposite of that idea?"

- **Put your ideas to work.** Try out an idea. If it doesn't work, keep trying. Figure out what part of the idea needs to change. Change it, then try again.

Use IT! **At school:** Write a science fiction story.

At home: Design a new game.

Set Goals

We all have dreams and goals. But sometimes they never become real. Here's how you can turn goals into accomplishments.

How can I achieve my goals?

▶ **Follow these steps:**

- Set a goal that is specific and realistic.
- List tasks that will get you to your goal.
- Research each task. Try to talk to someone who has met the same goal.
- Set a time frame for reaching your ultimate goal. Set deadlines for tasks along the way.

Use IT! **At school:** I want to run for student council.

At home: I want to train for a marathon.

Find a Mentor

We all have different talents and experiences. A mentor can provide advice and support to help you achieve your goals. Learn how to find a mentor who is right for you.

Who can help me get where I want to be?

▶ **Follow these steps:**

- **Identify a need.** What do you want a mentor to help you achieve?
- **Search for mentors.** At school, talk to teachers or counselors about finding a mentor. Outside of school, contact an organization that does the kind of work that interests you.
- **Make contact with your mentor.** Ask questions, and be specific about what you're looking for.
- **Create a plan.** Work with your mentor to create a plan for how he or she can help you achieve your goals.
- **Be courteous.** Always thank your mentor for his or her time.

Use IT! **At school:** Find a mentor who can help you improve your study habits.

At home: Find a mentor who can answer your questions about a career you're interested in.

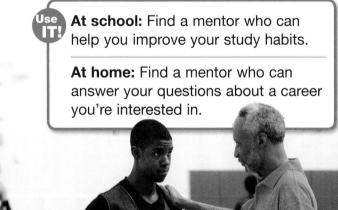

 ## Take Notes

How will you remember important information? Learn how to take and organize notes so you'll have easy access to the information you need.

How can I take good notes?

▶ **Follow these steps:**

- **Figure out what you need to know.** Do you need to remember dates in history? Steps in a process? Do you need to learn about an author?
- **Get the information you need.** Explore many sources: books, websites, videos, local experts, and more. Be sure to record your sources to avoid plagiarism.
- **Write it down.** As you listen or read, write down main points. Circle or underline what you most need to remember.
- **Organize.** While the information is still fresh, make sure you understand what you wrote or typed. Put your notes in an order you can use later.

Use IT! **At school:** Write a paper filled with interesting facts and ideas.

At home: Save important details about events or topics that matter to you.

Gather Information

We live in the Information Age. Technology tools bring a universe of information to our fingertips. Here's how to find the knowledge you need.

How do I get information I need?

▶ **Use these tips:**

- **Know what you need.** Get focused by framing your question or goal clearly.
- **Use a search engine.** Try different search terms to find sources online.
- **Use multiple methods.** Don't make the Internet the only place you look. Use library books, conduct a survey, or interview an expert.
- **Narrow down your choices.** Skim the resources you find to determine whether you should spend time reading them more closely.

 At school: Where can I find ideas for a great science project?

At home: Where have I seen this actor?

Search | China's Factories | Search

 # Analyze Media

You see thousands of media messages every day. Advertisements, newspapers, books, movies, websites— what are they telling you? Figure out the message behind the media.

What are they trying to tell me?

▶ **Ask yourself:**

- Who created the message, and why?
- What images and words do they use?
- What information and ideas are included in this message? What is left out?
- Should I believe their claims?

Use IT! **At school:** Research political campaign slogans.

At home: Figure out whether an ad's message is too good to be true.

YOU NEED TO BUY THIS TODAY!

Evaluate Sources

You can't believe everything you read. When it comes to both print and online sources, separate the useful from the useless.

Can I trust this information?

▶ **Ask yourself:**

- Is the source current? If it's a website, was it recently updated?
- Is the author or publisher an expert on the topic?
- Is the source unbiased? Does it seem to be in favor of one side over another?
- Does the content seem well written, well researched, and logical?

Use IT! **At school:** Find reliable sources for a report.

At home: Find a dependable review of that new video game.

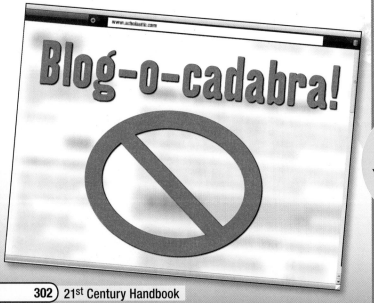

Analyze Information

Information is all around us. To put all that information to use, we need to think about what we are learning as we read or listen. Learn to analyze patterns of information.

What can I learn from this source?

▶ **Ask yourself:**

- What is the topic of this information?
- What is the main idea?
- How is this information organized? By cause and effect? Comparison and contrast? Problem and solution? Time order? Categories of different types?
- How new is this information? Is it similar to other things I've read or heard about this topic?

Use IT! **At school:** Understand science articles about complex topics such as medical robots.

At home: Read maps, recipes, instructions, and schedules.

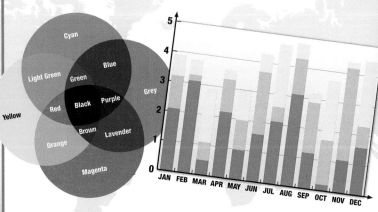

Use Technology for Communication

Technology keeps changing the way we communicate. So, we need to make sure we choose the tool that suits the message.

How can I share my ideas?

▶ **Use these tips:**

- Use texts and social networking for sharing with friends. Just be sure to protect your privacy.
- Email messages to employers, teachers, or anyone "official." For these emails, avoid using texting abbreviations and emoticons.
- Pick up the phone and call when a personal touch is needed.
- To share information and ideas, start a blog or a personal website.

 At school: Host a video conference with a class in another country.

At home: Create a fan website for your favorite book, actor, or musician.

Protect Yourself on the Internet

We practically live online. In fact, people spend hours every day emailing, chatting, surfing, or sharing updates, photos, videos, and more. Learn how to guard your privacy and safety.

How can I protect myself on the Internet?

▶ **Use these tips:**

- **Be cautious.** Don't open an email attachment unless you know who it's from and what the file is supposed to be.
- **Guard your personal data.** Never share your passwords. Don't reply to an email asking for personal or financial information, even if it seems official.
- **Report cyberbullying.** If you witness bullying online, report it to the website and tell a parent or teacher.
- **Use common sense.** Don't post photos, videos, or comments that could hurt your reputation or keep you from getting a job in the future.

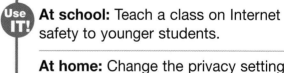 **At school:** Teach a class on Internet safety to younger students.

At home: Change the privacy settings on your Internet accounts.

rBook Workshop Log

▶ Fill in the dates as you start and complete each Workshop. Rate your effort on the Workshop using the Rating Scale. Record the date and your score for the *rSkills Test*. Then answer a final question about the Workshop.

Rating Scale			
needs improvement	average	good	excellent
①	②	③	④

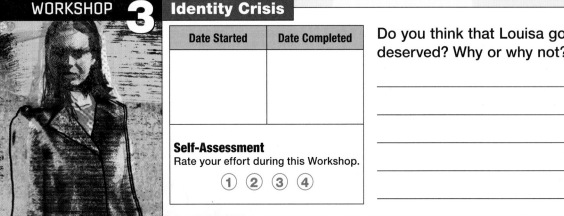

WORKSHOP 1 The New Americans

Date Started	Date Completed

Self-Assessment
Rate your effort during this Workshop.
① ② ③ ④

Which was your favorite reading in this Workshop?

❑ "School Before Soccer"

❑ "Fitting In"

❑ "A New Immigration Boom"

Why? _____

_____

rSkills Test   Date: _____   Score: _____

WORKSHOP 2 When Disaster Strikes

Date Started	Date Completed

Self-Assessment
Rate your effort during this Workshop.
① ② ③ ④

Which type of natural disaster would you *least* want to be caught in?

❑ a hurricane   ❑ a forest fire

❑ a lightning storm

Why? _____

_____

_____

rSkills Test   Date: _____   Score: _____

WORKSHOP 3 Identity Crisis

Date Started	Date Completed

Self-Assessment
Rate your effort during this Workshop.
① ② ③ ④

Do you think that Louisa got what she deserved? Why or why not?

_____

_____

_____

_____

_____

rSkills Test   Date: _____   Score: _____

WORKSHOP 4 — Stolen Childhoods

Date Started	Date Completed

Self-Assessment
Rate your effort during this Workshop.
(1) (2) (3) (4)

What will you remember most about this Workshop?

_____

_____

_____

_____

_____

_____

rSkills Test Date: _____ Score: _____

WORKSHOP 5 — Under Pressure

Date Started	Date Completed

Self-Assessment
Rate your effort during this Workshop.
(1) (2) (3) (4)

Who feels the most pressure at your school? Explain.

_____

_____

_____

_____

_____

_____

rSkills Test Date: _____ Score: _____

WORKSHOP 6 — Poe: The Master of Horror

Date Started	Date Completed

Self-Assessment
Rate your effort during this Workshop.
(1) (2) (3) (4)

What do you think was the creepiest part of "The Fall of the House of Usher"?

☐ Madeline Usher   ☐ the storm
☐ the burial vault   ☐ the house

Why? _____

_____

_____

_____

rSkills Test Date: _____ Score: _____

STUDENT LOG

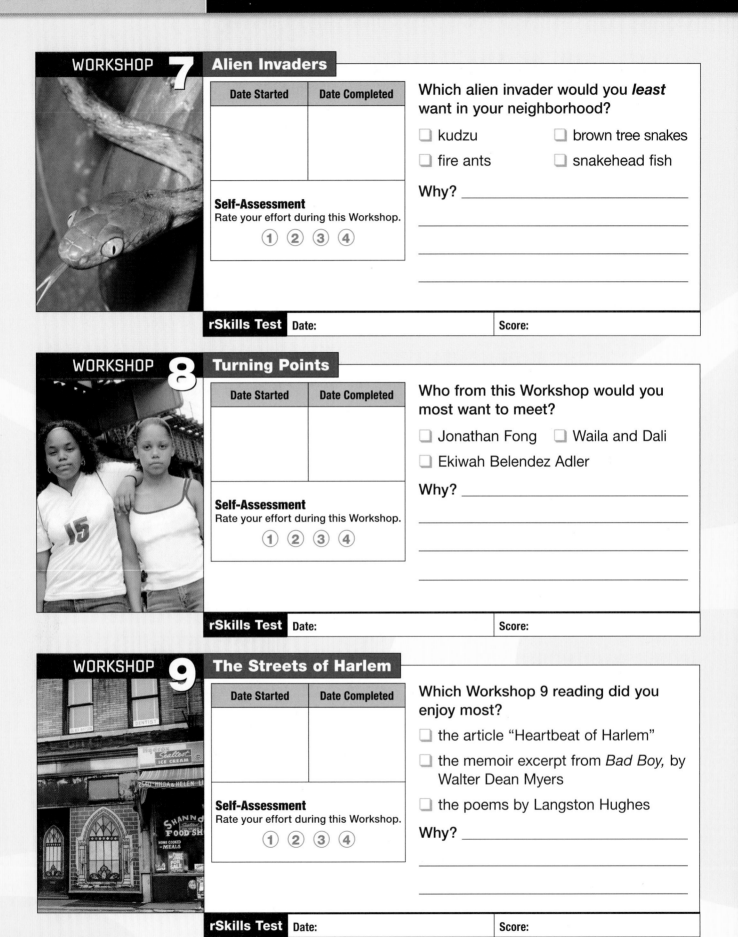

WORKSHOP 7 — Alien Invaders

Date Started	Date Completed

Self-Assessment
Rate your effort during this Workshop.
① ② ③ ④

Which alien invader would you *least* want in your neighborhood?

- ☐ kudzu
- ☐ brown tree snakes
- ☐ fire ants
- ☐ snakehead fish

Why? _____

_____

_____

_____

rSkills Test Date: _____ Score: _____

WORKSHOP 8 — Turning Points

Date Started	Date Completed

Self-Assessment
Rate your effort during this Workshop.
① ② ③ ④

Who from this Workshop would you most want to meet?

- ☐ Jonathan Fong
- ☐ Waila and Dali
- ☐ Ekiwah Belendez Adler

Why? _____

_____

_____

_____

rSkills Test Date: _____ Score: _____

WORKSHOP 9 — The Streets of Harlem

Date Started	Date Completed

Self-Assessment
Rate your effort during this Workshop.
① ② ③ ④

Which Workshop 9 reading did you enjoy most?

- ☐ the article "Heartbeat of Harlem"
- ☐ the memoir excerpt from *Bad Boy*, by Walter Dean Myers
- ☐ the poems by Langston Hughes

Why? _____

_____

_____

rSkills Test Date: _____ Score: _____

Topic Software Log

▶ Use these pages to keep track of the Topics you have completed. Check off each segment you finish. Then write a final statement about each Topic.

Topic 1 Art Attack

- ☐ 1.1 *Crop Art*
- ☐ 1.2 *Halls of Fame*
- ☐ 1.3 *Young at Art*
- ☐ 1.4 *STOMP*

My favorite segment was _____

_____

Topic 2 Disaster!

- ☐ 2.1 *Flood!*
- ☐ 2.2 *Earthquake!*
- ☐ 2.3 *Avalanche!*
- ☐ 2.4 *Volcano!*

I would recommend this Topic to _____

_____

Topic 3 Survive

- ☐ 3.1 *Braving Alaska*
- ☐ 3.2 *Out of the Dust*
- ☐ 3.3 *In Search of Rain*
- ☐ 3.4 *Take a Dive*

The most interesting thing I saw in this Topic was _____

_____

Topic 4 Help Wanted

- ☐ 4.1 *Jump Shot*
- ☐ 4.2 *In the Funnies*
- ☐ 4.3 *Building Dreams*
- ☐ 4.4 *Blast Off!*

The job that I learned about and want the most is _____

_____

Topic 5 Show Me the Money!

- ☐ 5.1 *Making Money*
- ☐ 5.2 *Bogus Bills*
- ☐ 5.3 *Fighting Forgery*
- ☐ 5.4 *Mangled Money*

One new thing I learned was _____

_____

Topic 6 *You and the Law*

- ☐ 6.1 *Ban the Boards*
- ☐ 6.2 *What Curfew?*
- ☐ 6.3 *No Passing*
- ☐ 6.4 *Taking Mom to the Mall*

One law I think should change is _____

_____

_____

Topic 7 *Beating the Odds*

- ☐ 7.1 *Feel the Beat*
- ☐ 7.2 *Second Chance*
- ☐ 7.3 *Little Rock Nine*
- ☐ 7.4 *Write Decision*

The person in this Topic I'd most like to meet is _____

_____

_____

Topic 8 *Extreme Sports*

- ☐ 8.1 *Extreme Snowboarding*
- ☐ 8.2 *Extreme Biking*
- ☐ 8.3 *Extreme Kayaking*
- ☐ 8.4 *Extreme Surfing*

The extreme sport I'd most want to try is _____

_____

_____

Topic 9 *The Whole World Watched*

- ☐ 9.1 *A Dark Day in Dallas*
- ☐ 9.2 *One Giant Leap*
- ☐ 9.3 *Freedom in South Africa*
- ☐ 9.4 *The People's Princess*

The person I admire the most from this Topic is _____

_____

_____

Topic 10 *Tales of Adventure*

- ☐ 10.1 *The Call of the Wild*
- ☐ 10.2 *Deep Freeze*
- ☐ 10.3 *A Man With a Mission*
- ☐ 10.4 *On Top of the World*

The most interesting person I learned about was _____

_____

_____

Topic 11 First Person

- ☐ 11.1 *A Timeless Voice*
- ☐ 11.2 *Sailing Into History*
- ☐ 11.3 *Bringing Up Baldo*
- ☐ 11.4 *Daughter of a Legend*

One new thing I learned was _____

_____

_____

Topic 12 Scene Stealers

- ☐ 12.1 *Prince of Salsa*
- ☐ 12.2 *Wrap Stars*
- ☐ 12.3 *Broadway for* Rent
- ☐ 12.4 *Wall to Wall*

The art or performance I'd really like to see in person is _____

_____

_____

Topic 13 Game On!

- ☐ 13.1 *Jump!*
- ☐ 13.2 *Big-League Dreams*
- ☐ 13.3 *On the Fast Track*
- ☐ 13.4 *Super Gamers*

My favorite segment was _____

_____

_____

Topic 14 Children of War

- ☐ 14.1 *Alive and Kicking*
- ☐ 14.2 *On the Safe Side*
- ☐ 14.3 *Rats to the Rescue*
- ☐ 14.4 *Ready to Roll*

I would recommend this Topic to _____

_____

_____

Topic 15 The Big Giveback

- ☐ 15.1 *Tunes 4 the Troops*
- ☐ 15.2 *Get Pumped!*
- ☐ 15.3 *Hometown Hero*
- ☐ 15.4 *Room to Read*

The most interesting thing I saw in this Topic was _____

_____

_____

Independent Reading Log

▶ **Use these pages to keep track of the books you read.**

- Write the book's title in the blank box. Add a design if you like.
- Fill in the dates as you start and complete each book.
- Mark what kind of book it is.
- Rate the book using the rating scale at right. Then write a statement about the book.

Rating Scale

★☆☆☆ = I didn't like it.
★★☆☆ = It was O.K.
★★★☆ = It was good.
★★★★ = It was great!

Date Started	Date Completed

☐ *READ 180* Paperback
☐ *READ 180* Audiobook
☐ Other Book

Rate the Book:
☆ ☆ ☆ ☆

I would recommend this book to _____
_____
_____

Date Started	Date Completed

☐ *READ 180* Paperback
☐ *READ 180* Audiobook
☐ Other Book

Rate the Book:
☆ ☆ ☆ ☆

The reason why I rated this book _____
_____
_____

Date Started	Date Completed

☐ *READ 180* Paperback
☐ *READ 180* Audiobook
☐ Other Book

Rate the Book:
☆ ☆ ☆ ☆

This book reminded me of _____
_____
_____

Date Started	Date Completed

☐ *READ 180* Paperback
☐ *READ 180* Audiobook
☐ Other Book

Rate the Book:
☆ ☆ ☆ ☆

I chose to read this book because _____
_____
_____

Date Started	Date Completed

☐ *READ 180* Paperback
☐ *READ 180* Audiobook
☐ Other Book

Rate the Book:
☆ ☆ ☆ ☆

One question I have for the author is _____
_____
_____

Date Started	Date Completed

☐ *READ 180* Paperback
☐ *READ 180* Audiobook
☐ Other Book

Rate the Book:
☆ ☆ ☆ ☆

I think I will/won't remember this book

because _____
_____

Date Started	Date Completed

☐ *READ 180* Paperback
☐ *READ 180* Audiobook
☐ Other Book

Rate the Book:
☆ ☆ ☆ ☆

The best part of this book was _____
_____
_____

Date Started	Date Completed

☐ *READ 180* Paperback
☐ *READ 180* Audiobook
☐ Other Book

Rate the Book:
☆ ☆ ☆ ☆

One new thing I learned in this book was ____
_____
_____

Date Started	Date Completed

☐ *READ 180* Paperback
☐ *READ 180* Audiobook
☐ Other Book

Rate the Book:
☆ ☆ ☆ ☆

If I were making this book into a movie, it

would star _____
_____

Date Started	Date Completed

☐ *READ 180* Paperback
☐ *READ 180* Audiobook
☐ Other Book

Rate the Book:
☆ ☆ ☆ ☆

This book was easy/hard to finish because
_____
_____

STUDENT LOG

Date Started	Date Completed

❑ *READ 180* Paperback
❑ *READ 180* Audiobook
❑ Other Book

Rate the Book:
☆☆☆☆

If I were making this book into a movie, it would star _____

_____

Date Started	Date Completed

❑ *READ 180* Paperback
❑ *READ 180* Audiobook
❑ Other Book

Rate the Book:
☆☆☆☆

When I first saw this book, I thought it would be _____

_____

Date Started	Date Completed

❑ *READ 180* Paperback
❑ *READ 180* Audiobook
❑ Other Book

Rate the Book:
☆☆☆☆

I'd recommend this book to _____

_____

_____

Date Started	Date Completed

❑ *READ 180* Paperback
❑ *READ 180* Audiobook
❑ Other Book

Rate the Book:
☆☆☆☆

Reading this book made me feel _____

_____

_____

Date Started	Date Completed

❑ *READ 180* Paperback
❑ *READ 180* Audiobook
❑ Other Book

Rate the Book:
☆☆☆☆

The most interesting thing about this book was _____

_____

Date Started	Date Completed

❑ *READ 180* Paperback
❑ *READ 180* Audiobook
❑ Other Book

Rate the Book:
☆☆☆☆

One fact I learned in this book is _____

_____

_____

Date Started	Date Completed

☐ *READ 180* Paperback
☐ *READ 180* Audiobook
☐ Other Book

Rate the Book:
★ ★ ★ ☆

The best thing about this book is _____

_____

_____

Date Started	Date Completed

☐ *READ 180* Paperback
☐ *READ 180* Audiobook
☐ Other Book

Rate the Book:
★ ★ ★ ☆

Three words that describe this book are _____

_____

_____

Date Started	Date Completed

☐ *READ 180* Paperback
☐ *READ 180* Audiobook
☐ Other Book

Rate the Book:
★ ★ ★ ☆

I would recommend this book to _____

_____

_____

Date Started	Date Completed

☐ *READ 180* Paperback
☐ *READ 180* Audiobook
☐ Other Book

Rate the Book:
★ ★ ★ ☆

This book should/should not have a sequel

because _____

_____

Date Started	Date Completed

☐ *READ 180* Paperback
☐ *READ 180* Audiobook
☐ Other Book

Rate the Book:
★ ★ ★ ☆

If I were making this book into a movie, it

would star _____

_____

Date Started	Date Completed

☐ *READ 180* Paperback
☐ *READ 180* Audiobook
☐ Other Book

Rate the Book:
★ ★ ★ ☆

One new thing I learned in this book is _____

_____

_____

STUDENT LOG

Date Started | Date Completed

☐ *READ 180* Paperback
☐ *READ 180* Audiobook
☐ Other Book

Rate the Book:
☆ ☆ ☆ ☆

If I were making this book into a movie, it would star _____

_____

Date Started | Date Completed

☐ *READ 180* Paperback
☐ *READ 180* Audiobook
☐ Other Book

Rate the Book:
☆ ☆ ☆ ☆

When I first saw this book, I thought it would be _____

_____

Date Started | Date Completed

☐ *READ 180* Paperback
☐ *READ 180* Audiobook
☐ Other Book

Rate the Book:
☆ ☆ ☆ ☆

I'd recommend this book to _____

_____

_____

Date Started | Date Completed

☐ *READ 180* Paperback
☐ *READ 180* Audiobook
☐ Other Book

Rate the Book:
☆ ☆ ☆ ☆

Reading this book made me feel_____

_____

Date Started | Date Completed

☐ *READ 180* Paperback
☐ *READ 180* Audiobook
☐ Other Book

Rate the Book:
☆ ☆ ☆ ☆

The most interesting thing about this book was _____

_____

Date Started | Date Completed

☐ *READ 180* Paperback
☐ *READ 180* Audiobook
☐ Other Book

Rate the Book:
☆ ☆ ☆ ☆

One fact I learned in this book is _____

_____

_____

Date Started	Date Completed

- ❏ *READ 180* Paperback
- ❏ *READ 180* Audiobook
- ❏ Other Book

Rate the Book:

☆ ☆ ☆ ☆

The best thing about this book is _____

_____

_____

Date Started	Date Completed

- ❏ *READ 180* Paperback
- ❏ *READ 180* Audiobook
- ❏ Other Book

Rate the Book:

☆ ☆ ☆ ☆

Three words that describe this book are _____

_____

Date Started	Date Completed

- ❏ *READ 180* Paperback
- ❏ *READ 180* Audiobook
- ❏ Other Book

Rate the Book:

☆ ☆ ☆ ☆

I would recommend this book to _____

_____

_____

Date Started	Date Completed

- ❏ *READ 180* Paperback
- ❏ *READ 180* Audiobook
- ❏ Other Book

Rate the Book:

☆ ☆ ☆ ☆

This book should/should not have a sequel

because _____

_____

Date Started	Date Completed

- ❏ *READ 180* Paperback
- ❏ *READ 180* Audiobook
- ❏ Other Book

Rate the Book:

☆ ☆ ☆ ☆

If I were making this book into a movie, it

would star _____

_____

Date Started	Date Completed

- ❏ *READ 180* Paperback
- ❏ *READ 180* Audiobook
- ❏ Other Book

Rate the Book:

☆ ☆ ☆ ☆

One new thing I learned in this book is _____

_____

_____

Keep Track of Your Success!

▶ Create a bar graph showing your SRI Lexile scores over the year.

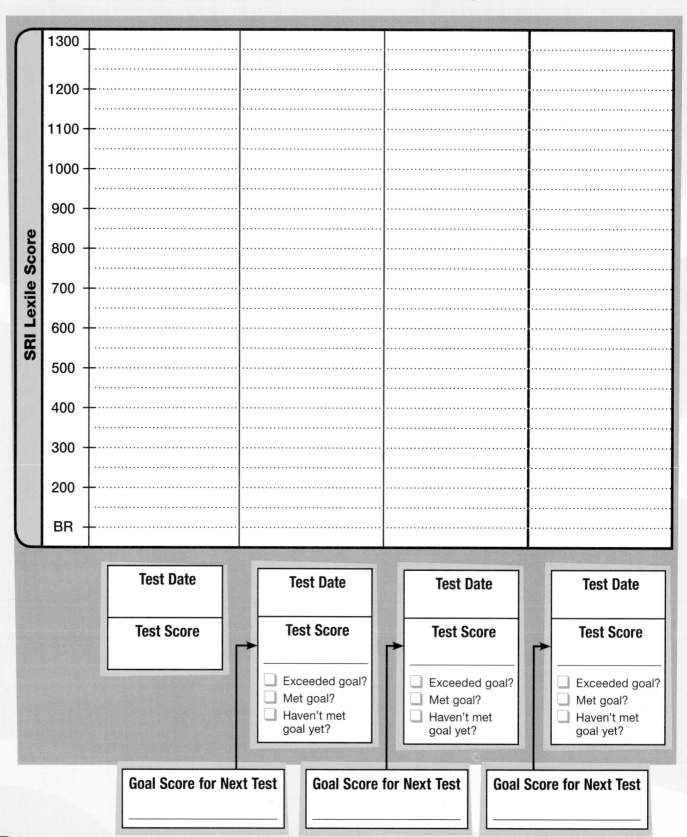

	Test Date	Test Date	Test Date	Test Date
	Test Score	**Test Score**	**Test Score**	**Test Score**
		☐ Exceeded goal? ☐ Met goal? ☐ Haven't met goal yet?	☐ Exceeded goal? ☐ Met goal? ☐ Haven't met goal yet?	☐ Exceeded goal? ☐ Met goal? ☐ Haven't met goal yet?

SRI Lexile Score

1300
1200
1100
1000
900
800
700
600
500
400
300
200
BR

Goal Score for Next Test

Goal Score for Next Test

Goal Score for Next Test

Workshop 1
The New Americans

Adapted from "Fitting In" by Jonathan Blum from *Scholastic Action* magazine, September 27, 2002. Copyright © 2002 by Scholastic Inc. All rights reserved.

Workshop 3
Identity Crisis

Adapted from "Louisa, Please Come Home" from *Come Along With Me* by Shirley Jackson. Copyright © 1960 by Shirley Jackson. Reprinted by permission of Viking Penguin, a division of Penguin Group (USA) Inc.

"I'm Nobody! Who Are You?" from *The Poems of Emily Dickinson*, edited by Thomas H. Johnson. Copyright © 1951, 1955, 1979 by the President and Fellows of Harvard College. Reprinted by permission of The Belknap Press of Harvard University Press and the Trustees of Amherst College.

"A Whole New Look" from *Skin Deep and Other Teenage Reflections* by Angela Shelf Medearis. Text copyright © 1995 by Angela Shelf Medearis. Reprinted by permission of Diva Productions, Inc.

Workshop 6
Poe: The Master of Horror

Adapted from "The Fall of the House of Usher" by Edgar Allan Poe in *Scholastic Action* magazine, October 15, 2001. Copyright © 2001 by Scholastic Inc. All rights reserved.

"The Haunted House" abridged from *Nightmares: Poems to Trouble Your Sleep* by Jack Prelutsky. Copyright © 1976 by Jack Prelutsky. Reprinted by permission of HarperCollins Publishers. All rights reserved.

Workshop 8
Turning Points

"The New Kid" adapted from "Moving from 'Cool Kid' to 'Foreign Kid'" by Jonathan Fong from *The New York Times Upfront* magazine, November 26, 2001. Copyright © 2001 by Scholastic Inc. and The New York Times Co. All rights reserved.

"A New Life—Through Poetry" adapted from "A Triumph of Talent" by Christy Damio from *Scholastic Action* magazine, April 5, 2004. Copyright © 2004 by Scholastic Inc. All rights reserved.

Abridged from "Nothing" from *Soy* by Ekiwah Belendez Adler. Reprinted by permission of the author. All rights reserved.

"Hard Time" adapted from "Our Mom Was in Jail" by Mona Mansour from *Scholastic Choices* magazine, November/December 2003. Copyright © 2003 by Scholastic Inc. All rights reserved.

Workshop 9
The Streets of Harlem

Adapted from *Bad Boy: A Memoir* by Walter Dean Myers. Copyright © 2001 by Walter Dean Myers. Reprinted by permission of HarperCollins Publishers. All rights reserved.

"Juke Box Love Song," "Harlem [2]," and "Dreams" from *The Collected Poems of Langston Hughes* by Langston Hughes. Copyright © 1994 by The Estate of Langston Hughes. Reprinted by permission of Random House, Inc.